The B Word.

Infertility and Other Conversations

Simona Altavilla Moss

Simona Altavilla Moss
The B Word: Infertility and Other Conversations

Copyright © 2021 by Simona Altavilla Moss

First edition

ISBN 978-1-954233-05-8

Book design: Stephanie MacDougall/LIND Studio
Editor: Elise Volkman
Publishing support: TSPA The Self Publishing Agency Inc.

Dedicated to those still in waiting.
May you find comfort, strength and peace.

The B Word.

Infertility and Other Conversations

"Truthfully, though, it felt like the *cruelest twist* that it was going to be such an uphill battle for *a child that was so wanted.*"
—Sonia, sister

Forward

If you bought this book, chances are you're experiencing infertility or someone close to you is. If you're truly reading this book, maybe you're reading to find comfort in this process, maybe you're reading to learn more about what might lie ahead for you, or maybe you're reading to just understand what someone is going through.

I hope what I've written brings you all of that. I want you to know that I've written this book as I've experienced each aspect of my journey. As I began my treatments I started writing and didn't stop until I felt I had shared every bit that was important to me. My journey may be similar to yours, and that's okay. My journey may be very different from yours, and that's okay. The important part here is that you're not alone and you will get through this.

If you are reading this for yourself, I hope this book helps you feel less alone. If you are reading this for a family member or friend, I hope this helps you understand a little more about what your loved one might be going through. This can't be a forbidden thing to talk about anymore, and it certainly can't be something to be ashamed about. The silence is what hurts the most. I hope you get to the point I got to, if you haven't already, where you can share your feelings and open up. It will help you move forward, whatever that may look like.

I'm writing this from my perspective only and I am no expert by *any* means. My purpose for this book is to share my experience, raise awareness, and help those who are suffering in silence. I don't want you to feel bad for me. I simply want you to understand what me, my family, and so many others are experiencing. We are expected to carry on with life while dealing with this heavy thing that should be so natural, but is the farthest thing from it. On this long, long journey I have come to realize that it truly is a miracle.

"It really *opened my eyes* to how we treat women of *child-bearing age.*"
—Sonia

Introduction

You know the sound nails on a chalkboard makes? That screech-ing, painful, make-you-shake-your-head-and-cringe sound? That is exactly what it was like for me when anything concerning the word "baby" came up.

People can be cruel, whether they mean to be or not. I think that's the hardest part of this: having to deal with them. Unless they're going through infertility, no one truly understands all of the curve balls thrown your way. They can imagine and think it is difficult, and it is, but it's so much more complicated than that. I know some people who ask questions genuinely mean well and want happiness for me and my family, but I also know there are people who don't have good intentions. The pressures, the expec-tations, the next step you're supposed to be doing in life; you're in a relationship, they ask when you're getting married; you get married and then there it is: the B word.

"When are you going to have a baby?"

It's like we pass the two year mark for any milestone and we are on to the next "thing" of society's life expectations.

My husband and I have been blessed to have a beautiful son. He's happy, healthy, and full of energy. When my son was close to turning two, that's when it all started:

"When's the next one on the way? Don't wait too long. You want them close in age!"

"Will you have any more?"

"You better get going with your husband tonight!"

"He really needs a sibling..."

Is there nothing else to talk about? These comments are so loaded; filled with heartache, sadness, anger, hope, frustration, emptiness, longing, love, hate, sorrow. The statements were like daggers to my heart because I so badly wanted to answer with, "YES! I want more. YES! I want them to be close in age. YES! I want my son to know what it's like to have a sibling because I know how amazing it is. YES! YES! YES!" But, unfortunately, the real answer was no.

"No, I don't have one on the way. No, I don't want a large age gap. No, I'm not pregnant. NO."

I love my son so much, I can't put it into words. He's the happiest, most lovable boy you'll ever meet. He's kind, has good manners (most of the time), likes to annoy the crap out of me with loud squeaky noises and hearing his voice echo through the house. He wants me all the time; bed time, nap time, play time, you name it. He loves to go to school, color, paint, build with blocks, put puzzles together, and more. It's wonderful. It's the best feeling in the world and I know how lucky I truly am.

I'm so thankful to have my son while so many women struggle to just have their first child. I know. I also know there are so many women out there that have "secondary infertility," which shares many of the same causes as primary infertility.[1] It's very difficult to understand how your body can make one beautiful baby, yet can't make another one.

Why is that? My first pregnancy wasn't that long ago and I got in better shape afterwards than I was before the pregnancy. What the hell?!

It doesn't make sense to me; especially when couples like my husband and myself have focused on our lifestyle. We exercise at least 4–5 times per week with running and walking (we used to only exercise 1-2 times per week). We eat healthier. We drink a ton of water and only have a couple of beers or glasses of wine per week. We don't smoke or do any drugs. We take our vitamins. We're good, honest, hard-working people. I don't get it.

If you told me before this that it would take 2 years or so before I would get pregnant, and that I would have a girl, I wouldn't have believed you. I may not have even believed in myself enough to continue to push through all of the treatments. But I did it somehow. It was a very hard road for me and my husband, but I'm proud of us for all that we did together. We will never forget this difficult time in our lives. It has changed us. There's no doubt about that. We are forever grateful for science, our doctors and nurses at RMA, and all of the support we received from our family and friends.

I don't know why it worked out the way it did. I don't have those answers; all I have is my experience. I know it may be hard to read that my story "ended" with a successful pregnancy and a healthy baby. My purpose for sharing my story though, is not to talk about only that, but to talk about all of the emotions and hard things with infertility. I want my story to bring you comfort, strength, and hope.

And so, here is my journey from start to "finish."

"So, we had fun *'trying'* and then more *'trying,'* until *'trying'* started to feel like a defeated effort."
—Vicki, friend from high school

The Beginning

We decided. Decided to try again for a second baby. This had to be a conversation, like a green flag to begin. Obviously, it takes two to tango here. I wanted more babies and my husband did, too. I didn't feel that our family was complete yet. *I* didn't feel complete yet.

I've always wanted two or three children. I grew up in a large, Italian family and it was the greatest as a child — it still is. Growing up, there were 13 of us cousins, and then there were the aunts, uncles, grandparents — and, of course, countless memories. I am the oldest of three, with a younger brother and sister. I loved every second of being surrounded by so many family members. We love each other and would do anything for one another, but we also keep it real. We were raised to be respectful, work hard, be responsible, and never give up. We also went to church every Sunday. My Nonna and Nonno, my mom's parents, were very religious. I believed they had a straight line to God, and I still believe that.

With that said, it was kind of expected that everyone would get married and have lots of babies when they grew up. No one ever thought it would be difficult to do those things, including me.

It all began in January of 2018. It was date night and my husband and I were at our favorite Italian restaurant. My son was going to turn two the following month and I had been thinking about it for a little while by then. My husband and I talked it through, drank some wine, and got excited to grow our family.

The first few months of negative pregnancy tests were not alarming to us since it took about 3-4 months to conceive our first child. We didn't think it would happen right away. We expected it would take around that or a bit longer now that we were in our 30s.

We didn't think it would take 6 months, 8 months, 10 months, more than a year, 2 years. I wrote this chapter in August of 2019 and I still wasn't pregnant. When it got to the 6–7 month marker and we still had negative results, deep down I already felt that something was wrong.

There are no words to describe what it's like to get your period month after month after month, when all you want is to be pregnant. When it comes to infertility, you feel like a *failure*. You want it so bad that you check everything in your lifestyle and make sure it's only beneficial to conceive. You exercise on a regular basis, you eat cleaner, you do more deep breathing, you drink more water, you go for peaceful walks, you try and be mindful of your relationships with family, friends, coworkers, you work harder at your job, you work harder at being a wife, you make sure you spend that quality time with your only child. You do more. But it's not enough.

It just exhausts you some days. Some days you want to cry — a lot. Some days you want to full-blown scream at everything and ugly cry every second of the day because no matter where you look, something reminds you of babies and pregnancy and that you don't have that. The way it feels is indescribable. You feel like you have just been gutted from your heart to your belly.

You can't help it. You feel like you've failed. Something won't let you be what you were created on this earth to be.

You can't create another baby? God, why? Don't you see I'm in pain? So, so much pain? I know you have a plan and I'm trying so very hard to have faith, but there are days when I am so mad at you. Days that I'm drained and done waiting. Days like when I get the phone call from my doctor's office that the test came back negative; "call back on day one" (day one of your period, for those who don't know). Yep, thanks for the reminder. I know the drill, as I hold back the tears of yet again being let down.

This puts me into a whole downward cycle for a bit. It takes time to wrap my head around the why and think back to what we did last month that maybe we could fix this month. I know that sounds crazy, but after you've been trying for so long that's what you think about.

Being a teacher doesn't help either. I'm constantly planning and trying to problem-solve, so I think I can do this too. But I know I can't.

I know we are trying to do all of the right things. I think that might be the hardest part; that we know we are doing everything possible to make the best possible environment for a baby and it's still not working. It drives you crazy, literally. You go down the rabbit hole of trying to find the reason why it didn't happen this month. After all of the medications, injections, patience, and hope you put your body through physically and mentally — it still wasn't enough. You feel like a failure. You feel like you did something wrong to cause this and you beat yourself up over it.

When I would look at my son during these moments, I'd think to myself, "Why can't I create a sibling for you?" It made my heart ache to see him and think that it wouldn't work out again.

It would make me process that yet another month had gone by. Now my babies would be … how many years and months apart? That's one of the things I would think about each time I would get the bad news or get my period. My son would be x many years apart from his sibling. What would their relationship be like? Would they be close or not get along at all because they were so far apart in age? So many questions and scenarios would run through my mind.

The pressures from the outside world don't help you feel any better either, that's for sure. Getting the questions about having another baby, or being told that I really shouldn't wait too long so they are close in age — *none* of those comments are helpful. They are only hurtful.

If only people knew what I had been going through. That's why I began writing this book. I knew I needed to write this when I was in the middle of treatments. I had just gotten another negative result from my nurse. I knew deep down that this was something I had to do. This book is meant to bring awareness to people of what is actually going on with so many women. It's to bring attention to something that is so much bigger than what society thinks. I also wanted to write this book to help people. I want to let women and men know: they're not alone in this.

"I remember being at work when
I received *the call...*"
—Vicki

Teaching

The end of summer is always busy for me; gearing up for the new school year, getting excited for a fresh new start. However, dealing with infertility put a damper on life itself. During that time, my joy wasn't at full force as it usually was.

I know not everyone is a teacher, but for those who are, you can relate. You have to give your all everyday — all day, especially with little ones. I teach second grade and in the beginning of the year they are more like first graders who need a lot of guidance and support. As the year goes on, they get better and better at becoming more independent.

Well, the year I came to find out I had secondary infertility, to top it all off, I got probably the hardest class I have ever had in my career. That whole independence thing didn't really happen. Each kid in this class had their own unique personality. Each of them needed something from me. There were behavioral needs, special education needs, emotional needs, academic needs — and then I had to teach the curriculum.

I had help through a Special Education (SPED) Teacher and an aide in my classroom every day, but most days were extremely draining and hard. Every day, I felt like I gave my all to these kids and I had nothing left to give after they left. I had to dig deep, so deep, to do my best teaching for them. It was my job and I didn't know how else to do it. It wasn't in my nature to give

50 percent or even 80 percent. I was raised and taught to always try and do my best no matter what and so that's what I did — until I was a little past halfway through the school year.

When the going got tough, I couldn't understand how I was still dealing with similar issues and how difficult it still was. It was February and I was close to burning out. Sure, did what I have going on in my personal life make it even harder to have my usual full-blown happiness and pep-in-my-step? Abso-fucking-lutely! But I kept my head up as high as I could and kept doing my job because those kids needed me. Even though I would deal with temper tantrums, talk-back attitudes, fear of getting hit, or just kids crying in the middle of a lesson because they didn't understand it right away, I pushed through. I got used to having administration in and out of my room, the door opening and closing all the time. I had to adjust big time.

The "Calming Corner" was utilized often. If you don't know what that is, go on Pinterest. You'll find a ton of resources. I used to call it the "Calm Caddy," which had different tools to help students calm down, like stress balls, a Rubix cube, and legos. They use a timer and once the time is up they have to come back to join the class. Let me tell ya, I used that corner just as much as the kids did that year!

It was a difficult year to say the least. I couldn't just go in to work an hour late or leave an hour early like some people may be able to do in other careers. I had to be clocked in by 8:25 each morning and could not leave until 3:40 each afternoon, excluding every Monday, which were meeting days and we stayed until 4:40 pm.

The good thing was that the Reproductive Medicine Associates (RMA), the clinic where I went for tests, blood work, and ultrasounds, worked around people who had jobs. They opened at 6 am so that you could go get your blood work and ultra-sounds and whatever else done before work without having to take time off. Thank God for that. However, when you have to go in multiple times a week or month, you don't get lucky every time. You're not the only one doing the same thing. There were multiple days when it was backed up by at least a half hour. I was 40 minutes away from work so I was on a tight schedule. I was always rushing, rushing, rushing. It brought my blood pressure up big time, which I'm sure didn't help the situation.

Eventually, I had to tell my boss what was going on because I was coming in late a couple times a week. I'm always one to be honest and upfront; I think it serves you best no matter the situation. Of course, my boss was very supportive and I was so appreciative of that. It put me more at ease.

But I also didn't like being late to work. Each morning was a juggle to get out the door. My husband and I had to take turns taking my son to daycare when I had to go in to get monitored, which threw off everything. It meant we had to wake up that much earlier; get everything ready to go that much quicker. It was hard to basically run a marathon before I even got to work for a full day of teaching. There was always so much to do and not enough time. There was no room for relaxing or easing into my day.

Once it was time to begin shots and be on a schedule, I had to do even more planning and coordinating. I was starting Ovulation Induction (OI) injections, which help produce multiple eggs, thereby increasing chances of conception. By this time, it was the end of the school year. Thankfully, work was slowly coming to a wrap. However, the stress of starting something new and intense didn't help my mental health at all.

I don't think I was really happy that school year. Everything was just a mess, for me at least. I had so much going on in my head with trying to juggle my life and trying to be strong as a teacher, especially for that class because I knew they needed more. You could say I ran myself into the ground by trying to give 100 percent in every "job" that I had, which in turn made me nuts. I definitely didn't give 100 percent to each part of me because that's just impossible. I know this now.

The shots, the routine blood work, and the ultrasounds continued throughout the summer, and throughout the next fall and winter as well. For each phase of treatments, the amount of times I had to go in for monitoring varied. Monitoring is what we "infertiles" call the wee morning hours of blood draws, ultrasounds, pelvic checks — the whole shebang. Yes, bright and early, we would have all this done, several times a week sometimes.

In the beginning, when I started off just taking Clomid pills, monitoring happened maybe once a week or every other week. Then, the next phase I went in a little more, maybe once a week. Once I started the intrauterine insemination (IUI) process, it was even more — about 1–2 times a week. Eventually, it was 2–3 times a week, especially when I began in vitro fertilization (IVF).

With each phase, it was more because the process was more. More medications were involved, therefore more monitoring needed to happen to make sure my body was responding appropriately. If it didn't, that cycle could be a waste (and yes, that happened once).

All of this meant starting another school year without being pregnant and with added stress on my plate. I wanted the summer to be my saving grace so I wouldn't have to worry about so many appointments, medications, and so on while I was working. However, my plan isn't always the plan. We continued to move forward, and I tried to start fresh that school year.

I told myself it was a new class, a new year, and it was going to be good. It was a great class full of kids with such wonderful personalities. I think I was scarred, though, from the previous year. I had to learn to let go and be the happy, loving teacher I used to be. I told myself I had to try my hardest to go easy on myself. I think I did, but it took time.

That September I had my second IUI, then began the process of IVF in October. It all began with the retrieval. All I do is cringe when I think back to these times. The shipments that would come in from the specialized pharmacy would begin my worry and trigger the fear. There was just so much stuff. So many syringes, needles, bottles of medication, boxes of other types of medication, gauze pads, bandaids, alcohol swabs, and directions. It was very overwhelming.

One thing I did appreciate was that the pharmacy (Schrafts 2.0, highly recommended) always had a sticker on the inside of the boxes with a number and a phrase that said something like, "Feeling overwhelmed? It's okay, give us a call." It just made me think that I wasn't the only one feeling that way. These shipments for the IVF process definitely had the most medications compared to the previous procedures we did. It was nerve-racking.

There were several steps. To sum them up, I had to take medications to get my body ready for the retrieval procedure. After the retrieval, I had to wait about a month or so. Specifically, I needed to wait until another cycle came and went — I had to get my period again. Once that happened, I took more medications to get my body ready for a transfer.

For both the retrieval and transfer, I had to take a couple days off of work each time — another stressor for me. I hated taking time off, period. As a teacher, it's not easy calling in sick or taking a day off. It's more work to be out than to be there. I also didn't like being away from the kids and having their routines thrown off. It's always different with a substitute teacher, even when you have awesome ones. I had to type up my plans and get all of the materials together for 1–2 days each time. I also had to coordinate with my coworkers to assist while I was out.

Additionally, my son was attending Pre-K at my school at the time, which made it difficult when I had procedures. I needed him to go to school so that I could rest at home on these days and not have to get up and down to take care of him. Of course, my husband left an hour earlier than I did in the morning, so that was another arrangement.

Thank heaven for my good friend, Stacey. She saved me on so many occasions and Tyler adored her. She would pick him up in the morning, play with him before school started, and bring him home once school was over. I sincerely appreciated these favors, as she also had to get her own classroom ready before her students arrived.

There were so many people who helped me along the way. As the saying goes for parenthood, "It takes a village," it also goes for teaching. I am so thankful to all of my coworkers and friends for everything they did for me. I will always appreciate their help during those times.

It was hard, though. I never knew the meaning of multitasking and juggling until this all fell into my lap. Those days came and went and at some point it began feeling like it wasn't worth it.

We got the negative results after that transfer. I was absolutely numb. I went into a state of darkness. It was right around Thanksgiving and everyone was gearing up for the holidays, which just made it even harder for me. I was so disappointed in everything. But I continued to go in each day and do my job. I think by this time, I was coming around to the fact that the end was near and I had to brace myself for the possibility that this just wasn't going to happen. I think I tried to adjust my lifestyle to having an only child and being content with what I had. Every time I would see Tyler at school, I would tear up inside. He got along so well with other kids; he was so social and just so happy. It ate away at me that I couldn't give him a sibling.

I don't know how, but I managed to only have to deal with taking a shot one time during school hours. Thank God it was only one time because, boy, was it stressful! Again, being a teacher you can't just walk in and take your time grabbing a cup of coffee, and start your day off checking emails. The kids show up at 8:40 am and leave at 3:15 pm. Yes, I have a lunch break and one prep a day, but it's all on a rigid schedule.

One part of my treatments required taking certain shots at exactly the same time every day, am and pm. The time, of course, was 8:40 am on the dot. Perfect! The same time my kids arrived! This was not a time that I got to choose, either. It was a specific direction from my nurse.

Again, I had to coordinate. At first, I thought I'd just do the shot in the staff bathroom. All I needed was a small place to put the bag down (I used my lunchbox to hold all the meds and tools I needed). Then, my brain decided to work and I contacted my nurse. I filled her in on what was going on the night before and she was so supportive. I had to arrange for someone to bring my son to his class and for someone to take care of my class for the first ten minutes of the day. It was a lot of thinking and planning just to get this one shot down; this one very important shot.

Not only was it a lot to physically get all those ducks in a row, but it was also mentally draining. It felt weird to be in the hallway during morning arrival because I normally had my students coming into my classroom. I never had hallway duty. In my mind, I was thinking, "People are looking at me, wondering what the heck I'm doing and why I'm going to the nurse's office."

Yes, that's where my mind went, especially because it's a small school and people talk. I was even more self-conscious about the things I did and how I looked during this time. All the meds made me put on extra pounds, which didn't help the situation.

After making sure all arrangements for my students and my son were taken care of, then I had to do the task at hand: administer the injection. I walked into the nurse's office, went to one of the rooms, and closed the door. I set up all of the materials I would need and then started my music playlist to calm my mind.

This was *all* before starting my work day. I still amaze myself.

Queue Britney Spears, "Work Bitch," and I started my process: wash hands, prepare the syringe with medicine, make sure it's the correct dosage, clean the site with an alcohol swab, squeeze a chunk of skin to stick the needle into, count down, and stick it!

That was the worst part. It usually took me a few rounds of counting down from three to actually do it. Once I did, I pushed the syringe so all the medication went in, then counted to 10 before taking out the needle. I had my sharps container there to dispose of the needle and voilà! I was done.

I took a moment to just breathe and, of course, I started to cry. I just couldn't believe that I was still doing this. I couldn't believe that I was sitting in my school nurse's office giving myself a freakin' shot because I still wasn't pregnant. I couldn't believe any of it. I was sad for myself and also pissed off. In my head, I prayed that it would work out the way it was supposed to.

We had opened up to pretty much everyone we knew by the early fall of 2019. I had been informing family and friends about each step along the way, but I quickly regretted that. It became too much to deal with. We received so many questions and well-wishes. I knew everyone meant well and they wanted to be there for support; however, I felt that each time I said something, it was taking more energy out of me than it was reviving in me.

I think it felt this way because it wasn't anything positive. I was running out of hope and I just couldn't listen to one more person try to give me positive advice, especially because they had literally no idea what I physically and mentally had to do each day. I know it wasn't their fault, but I also knew I didn't want to do this anymore. My husband and I had talked it through and decided we weren't going to share anything more about our journey until we wanted to either share happy news or the "end" of our journey.

That first transfer didn't work. Our first embryo didn't make it. We had lost our first possible baby. It was really difficult to wrap our heads around it. After that hard blow, I had really lost almost all hope in it. I really thought IVF would be the golden ticket and after that it was really hard to stay positive. I went back to my state of closing everything and everyone off. I just told people to not ask me any more questions. I would give them details if I was able to. I had to stop sharing and stop talking about it with others who didn't know what it was like. It was just too emotional. I was back to tearing up or getting angry at the thought of it all.

It was so hard to continue to move forward, teach, and go about daily life. In the back of my mind I felt that it just wasn't in the cards for us. The loss of our first embryo happened around Thanksgiving of 2019. Since it was the holiday season, it made everything a little bit harder than it already was. It was a time of celebration and cheer, but that was the opposite of what I was feeling. At school, the kids could only think of Christmas and Santa and excitement. I had to put on my happy face and do the whole shebang.

At this point I had two options: try all the embryos, or stop. I knew that if I didn't transfer those embryos, I would regret it forever. This meant I had to do another transfer, and if that didn't work, one more after that. This meant more rounds of injections and medications. This meant doing everything all over ... again.

I can't tell you how frustrating this all was. I was thankful that I had an easier class that year. It made my brain feel a little lighter with the day-to-day workload for sure. This time going in, my second transfer would be over winter break; the day before Christmas Eve to be exact. I thought to myself, "Maybe it'll make a difference — not having to worry about work and setting up plans for days and worrying about being out of school again." I hoped and prayed it would make a difference ... and that Santa might bring me a little Christmas magic.

"It was prayer and *sometimes yelling* at God that got me through the tough moments, but it was also having an *under-standing therapist* of my own to process through this *emotional trauma.*"

—Vicki

Therapy

I know there are support groups out there. RMA offers several different webinars and meeting groups for every aspect of infertility. I'm sure they're amazing and so helpful, but they just weren't for me. I wasn't ready to openly talk about infertility because I thought it would make me vulnerable. For me, it felt like going to these sessions would open the door to other comments and questions, and I thought I'd had my fair share of those.

You might be thinking, "Why did you write this, then?" I wrote this as more of a journal for myself, or at least that's why I started. It's kind of like therapy to jot down my thoughts. There aren't many people I can or want to talk with about this. I talk to my therapist, yes, but not many others.

I realized about a year into trying to conceive that the process was tearing me up inside, affecting my life big time, and I knew I needed help. I reached out to my school counselor to see if she had any recommendations of therapists, without giving her too much information. She told me about a group close by and I ended up really connecting with the first therapist I tried. She was great. She just listened to everything I had to say in the beginning. Of course, the first two sessions I pretty much cried for a straight hour, but I guess I needed that. We discussed more than just my infertility. I shared my family history, my parents' divorce, my relationship with my dad, my relationship with my mom, my brother, my sister and also the distance between me and my family. Apparently that was something that really dug at me too.

I live in central New Jersey. My entire family, who I'm very close with, lives in Connecticut. When I was younger, about 16 years old, my parents got divorced. It may sound like no big deal now because so many families have experienced this, but it was terrible then and it still is a difficult piece of my life now, over 20 years later. I was a mess then, a teenager about to get my license, close with my dad, my world being torn apart when all my hormones were already enough to handle at that time. My parents tried talking to me, asking me to go see a therapist. I refused, but somehow they took me anyway, even though I kicked and screamed about it.

I'm thankful I went. The beginning was rough. I remember sessions with my dad too; trying to express my feelings, but also not wanting to speak to him. Session after session, we went. We talked about God-knows-what. I don't remember every conversation, but what I do remember is that it helped me. As stubborn as I was, it got me through a very difficult time. I should have continued going once I went to college and thereafter, but I didn't. Therapy is good for anyone, even if you don't have "serious" issues going on in your life.

I think there's a really bad stigma that goes along with therapy and "talking to someone" and it's unfortunate. I can say I used to be one of those people who thought negatively about it, but I'm here to tell you that it can actually save you. It can save you from yourself. It can save you from losing your mind. It can save you from going down a rabbit hole. It can save you from depression and anything else you may be suffering from. I believe in the power of therapy and I hope you give it a chance too. Therapy did save me and it still does.

One thing I learned, though, is that a therapist doesn't just magically make all your problems go away. You need to work for it. It's your life and you have to help make it what you want. A therapist can help guide you and give you advice, but they can't do the actual work for you — that's on you. It was hard in the beginning, and it's still a process.

Fast forward to being in therapy while dealing with infertility. I was in a bad place. The combination of having a busy toddler, working full time, being a wife, taking care of a house, and wrapping my head around secondary infertility took a huge toll on me. I never wanted to admit or face the reality of what I actually had on my plate. I never wanted to say that I had a lot going on or that I couldn't handle it all. Typing that out and reading it makes me realize that it's a lot for anyone. I remember my therapist telling me to give myself some credit; that it was okay to feel that way and have those emotions and outbursts. Just hearing someone who wasn't related to me or a friend of mine say that made me feel a world of a difference.

Even after becoming pregnant with my second child, I still go because life is hard no matter how you slice it. Therapy is like my hour of tension release, to let out whatever is on my mind. It makes me feel better. That's the bottom line. I talk about my worries, my fears, my son, my husband, my job, the future, my family — you name it.

My point in all of this is that if you are at a point in your life where you are bottling it all up inside, I get it. I understand. It's not easy to open your life up to some stranger to be judged. But therapy isn't like that. I just want to tell you that what you're feeling is okay and that in your own time, when you're ready, I hope you get the chance to talk to someone; whether it's a therapist, an infertility group, a journal — anyone who or anything that makes you feel better about yourself. This shit is hard and I know now: it's not meant to be lived through alone.

"I found *my faith.* I can't remember a time in which I *prayed* so much and *cried* to God just asking him to *help me through.*"
—Vicki

Faith and Hope

You may be thinking, "What the hell do faith and hope have to do with it?" or maybe you're thinking, "Fuck faith. It hasn't helped me this far!" I feel ya sister. I've been there, lived by that for quite some time. I didn't want to believe that there was something more than me, my husband, and science to help make my baby. You may not believe in God, and if not, totally skip ahead — I understand. For those who do believe in God, or who are maybe just curious, my faith has been a part of the process too, and I want to share that part with you.

For a long, long time I was full-blown furious with God. I couldn't understand why He was letting this happen to me. Why was He allowing me to endure so much pain, when all I wanted was happiness? I shut down my faith, I closed Him out for months and months on end. I didn't want to believe that there was another plan other than mine. I remember every month of failure, I would recalculate my maternity leave for if I got pregnant the next month and how it would affect my teaching schedule. I couldn't help myself. I'm a planner, a type-A personality, and I like to have everything in order. Each month when I would get a negative test back, my plans would be messed up again, so I continued to be angry, frustrated, and sad for a long period of time.

You think you have your whole life planned out, and then something smacks you straight in the face and wakes you up to reality. You know what I mean, especially if you're going through infertility. There's no guarantee for anything in life. I've realized that the hard way with all of this, unfortunately. On the flip side, I've also found comfort in knowing that God has a plan whether I like it or not. What helped me feel better was knowing that I've done and continue to do everything in my power and the rest is up to Him. That was what brought me down from my anger; what made me breathe with a sigh of relief. I had to put my faith in Him and trust that He would fulfill whatever I was meant to do and be.

That wasn't always the case. It took me a long, long time to get to this point; several months of anger, depression, sadness — all the emotional highs and lows. There were so many times I cursed Him out, screamed "What the fuck!"and didn't believe in Him since I was going through so much hell. How could He let this keep happening to me after watching me, my husband and my family go through so much pain? I just couldn't believe I was supposed to endure this.

There was a moment in August of 2019, when I had a big revelation of letting go. There came a time that I (sort of) let go of my anger and just left it up to "fate." I was driving by myself up to Connecticut, going to a family event, and in the middle of my ride as I was lost in thought and my music, I just had this wave of relief come over me. It literally felt like chills all over my body. I can't even remember what song was playing, but it must have been a good one. I remember thinking to myself, "Just let it all go." You can call me crazy, but it was as if someone was telling me to stop worrying, stop stressing, and leave it up to God. It was the strangest thing, but also the most exhilarating feeling.

I think it relates to a quote I came across on my journey: "Most people are about as happy as they choose to be." It made me think about how angry I had been and how much that had weighed on me. I slowly started to let go of the resentment and madness I had bottled up inside me. Some days, I choose to live by that, and other days, I'm just human! We all have our moments, our days, our time periods in life where we struggle. However, it's when we pick ourselves back up from the bottom of those pits that we can create something more beautiful than we could ever imagine.

The only thing? You have to work for it. You have to give yourself time. You have to give yourself some freakin' slack. You have to breathe. And maybe, just maybe, you have to believe.

You don't have to believe in God. You can believe in whatever it is you want to believe in. I don't go to church every week, or every month for that matter. (Don't tell my grandmother.) However, even though I may not be a perfect, practicing Catholic, that doesn't mean I don't have faith; that I don't pray or that I don't believe. If this journey has taught me one thing, it has taught me that God works in mysterious ways. We don't get to plan out every detail of our life, unfortunately. We may be able to work hard and try our best to achieve something, but He might have a different plan for us.

The worry started when we were still trying to get pregnant after 6 months. I knew deep down inside that something wasn't right. From then on, I just kept worrying. Did that play a factor in everything? Maybe, maybe not. I can't help the worry. It's the way I am. I think it's because I care too much. Or maybe I'm just neurotic! I get it from my Nonna (Italian for grandma) who worries about everything and then backs it up with prayers. So, that's what I would do: worry and then pray. It was all I could do.

I felt as if we were doing everything in our power to help create a healthy baby, but month after month it just wasn't working.

It was hard. Hard trying to believe that there was a plan for us that would be our future. I couldn't let go of the fact that the plan that I wanted may not be the plan that God had for me. It took me many, many months to get to the point where I trusted God and knew that whatever was meant to be was meant to be. That song, "If It's Meant to Be" by Florida Georgia Line and Bebe Rexa, was a painful one to listen to by the way! When that song came on the radio, all I could think was, "What if it's not meant to be?" What if Tyler would be my only child? I wasn't ready to accept that. I wanted more — more for him, more for me, more for our family.

Then there's hope. Hope. That was a son of a bitch. Let me explain. Hope gives you this positive, uplifting feeling. It makes you feel like there's a light at the end of the tunnel, and, believe me, I wanted to believe in that. I had hope almost every month for maybe the first year and a half of our journey. I believe I'm a positive person and I tried to stay on the bright side each time around, but it got old and hard after a while. My husband probably carried the majority of our hope as things dragged on. It was draining, month after month after month, to try to have that optimism and belief that it could be the one time it worked.

When I think back about this, I think of a boxer getting hit over and over again, just trying to make it. You want to be that underdog who rises up, but you just don't know if you have it in you to throw that knockout punch when you've been beaten down over and over again.

Another thing that drained my hope and faith throughout this was the empty room in the house that we had waiting.

Every single day, I'd walk by our empty "guest room," which wasn't really that anymore. It was *the* room — the one that would be the next baby's room — but we wouldn't say it out loud very much. My husband and I discussed years ago that it would be our second child's room and we had arranged the other bedrooms so that it worked out that way. We were lucky to have four bedrooms: the master bedroom, my son's bedroom, a larger room that we made the guest room/craft room and then there was the empty room. The empty room that didn't have a bed or anything for guests; it was just there. We had put the rocking chair in there that I no longer needed for my son and put other baby items in the closet for storage. The room was there as a reminder, basically. A reminder that we didn't have another baby; that we weren't pregnant. A reminder of the emptiness inside of me; inside of us. A reminder that this still wasn't working as we planned.

The other room, the larger "guest room," was my favorite spot during those days. It's where I would go to write and it's also my craft room. The space was like my own little sanctuary where I went just to get away. It's upstairs, away from the noise. It overlooks our backyard, which has a rock wall and a big hill with trees and bushes. The area brings so many birds, butterflies and wildlife. It's probably my favorite thing to do; to just sit and stare out the window.

In 2018, my husband and I planted a ton of wildflowers to beautify the hill. Once those finally started appearing in the late summer, I could just stare at all of it for hours. It brought so many more butterflies and birds; especially hummingbirds. I love flowers and I love wildlife. I mean, I'm no outdoorsy kind of girl, but I can thoroughly enjoy nature — from a distance. Staring out at the hill and watching all this happen with my window open, feeling the fresh breeze; it would make me feel more at peace. I stare at this same hill now and it's still my favorite spot. I feel like it lets me pause time for a little bit. It's private, I don't see any cars driving by, I don't see any people, and I just sit in the moment. I can just think.

Looking out into this backyard of mine now, after being pregnant for the second time and writing this book, reminds me of all the times I got those phone calls with bad news from the nurse or my doctor. I would come to my craft room, play my music, close the door, and cry. I'd stare out at the hill and run the millions of questions through my head. I'd write, paint, craft; I'd do whatever it was to get me through it. As I said, it took days to get out of those funks. But being in that space just helped me work through those moments. The view of the hill brought peace to me no matter when I needed it. It reminds me now of all the struggles I went through and I'll never forget them.

I believe in signs from above. It's probably due to how I was raised. I do believe in God; that there are guardian angels and higher powers out there. And even though I don't go to church every Sunday, I do believe in prayer. Of course, I had my doubts along the way; whether my prayers were even being heard. After exploring more on social media and learning more about infertility, I've read so many things that speak to me that I wish I had read earlier when I was in the thick of it. It could have made me feel better, or at least made me feel less alone. I'm so happy to have found such a large community of women out there.

It makes me feel better even now, after getting pregnant, to know that these women are not going through it alone. I saw a video recently of a husband giving his wife her trigger shot right in the belly. As much as I twinged and I flashed back to my moments of pain, I felt comforted in a weird way. Life can surprise you in ways you never thought possible when you open up your mind and accept who you are and what you have. It may be really difficult to hear that and actually believe it at times, but it's true.

"It was *terrible*. I could see how painful it was every time. You were *bruising* from them and had to keep sticking yourself in the same bruised areas re-peatedly, nevermind the *burning sensation* afterward. I obviously couldn't take the *pain away*, but I tried to make everything else about it *as fun as possible*. And I just kept praying every time that after all of this, it would be *successful*."

—Sonia

Doctor's Orders

We've always had exercise as a part of our routines, but got better at it over the years. My husband became an avid runner in the middle of our journey. He would always run or exercise and he became stronger and faster over time. He ran his first half marathon in October of 2018 and was incredible. Naturally, I joined the bandwagon and got better at running more often and faster, whether it was outdoors or on the treadmill.

When he did the half, I did the 5K. Running has become a stress-reliever for both of us. I never thought I would say that in my entire life since I hated exercise, especially running, when I was younger. Now, I don't know life without it. It was a release for me; a release to get my emotions out; a release of the anger built up inside me. I needed it at least four times a week, sometimes more if I had it in me. Until I was told I couldn't run, per doctor's orders, which made this journey even harder than it already was.

With the medications I had started, it was simple. "First phase" was the Clomid pills for five days, then the Ovidrel trigger shot, then timed intercourse. Along with starting medication, I had to be monitored with blood work and ultrasounds.

It doesn't sound like much, and in the beginning it wasn't. Then, that round didn't work so we did another. Of course, the second round didn't work either. Might I mention that I also hate needles, and blood. And here I was getting routine blood work and injecting myself with a needle at night. Even though my husband is a big strong man, he can't handle needles — the sight, the thought, nothing. He has fainted on multiple occasions of getting shots. Therefore, me, Miss America, had to give herself a shot — not once, but multiple times. I thought every time, "Okay, this will be the last one, you can do it."

Little did I know then that it wasn't even close.

I got to the second phase, which brought on stronger drugs and more monitoring. I was in and out of my doctor's office every few days. Even though that place is a beacon of hope, it also makes me think of all the let downs. It's exhausting just having to schedule and plan the morning of drop-offs, rushing to get to work on time, and having to mentally compartmentalize what I just did at 7 am before I even started my work day.

The second phase was 8–12 nights of injections that helped to grow my follicles, followed by the trigger shot. During this time period, I had to get blood drawn multiple times, along with ultrasounds, to monitor my levels and check the sizes of my follicles. This was to make sure they were growing at the right pace and measuring when the best night of injection would be for my trigger shot.

Now, I briefly mentioned it in the first phase, but you have to time out intercourse as well. After that trigger shot, my nurse gave us a time frame to take the shot and then a time frame for when to have sex afterward, for the next two nights in a row. You may be thinking, "Woohoo! Two nights of sex! Amazing!" But it's nothing like that.

We tried to shut off our brains and tried not to think about what we were trying to achieve; to think, "Ok let's just focus on us and enjoy this." Ladies and gents, if you're going through or have gone through this, you know it's nothing like that. How can you possibly not think about the end goal? How can you not have pressure weighing on your minds and your hearts? It's crazy not to! But hey, if you can, all the power to ya because you're better than me!

You try not to remember that you've failed multiple times before. You try to believe that this time will be different, but then it ends the same way. We did two rounds of this; in other words, we did this for about two months. It doesn't sound like that long or that many trials, but it feels like eternity when all you do is pray every day for it to work.

Phase three, or the fifth month of fertility drugs, was IUI (intrauterine insemination). It involved doing the injections again for about ten nights — ten straight — getting blood work, ultrasounds, and driving back and forth to the doctor's. Then the trigger shot night came, and I took it as I usually do. The next two mornings my husband had to go in to give his sperm donation and then I went in shortly after to be inseminated. It took minutes, if that, and it was, like, no big deal. The hardest part was getting the clamp put in, almost like getting a pap smear.

And every single day of the process, especially the days of insemination, I waited and hoped and prayed.

When I wrote this, I had just received the call from my nurse a few hours ago telling me that my pregnancy test was negative. You might know what happens after that. Everything inside you just crumbles, you cry hysterically, you scream, you yell at God, you think of what could've been and what's not. You're angry, you're terribly sad, you're everything.

I'm a very emotional person, I wear my heart on my sleeve and it's hard for me to hide the way I feel. Throughout this journey, I have been on one emotional roller coaster. It took me a few days after getting my period, or getting the negative result call, to get back on my feet. It took a lot out of me; it took me a while to wrap my head around it all; to be able to put the pieces back together and regain my strength, or at least as much as I was able to.

This was when I tried to think of all the positive things in my life and smack some perspective into my face. I've definitely literally smacked myself in the face to get with it. As I wrote this, I was in my craft room typing away, looking out my window at the butterflies flying around my wildflowers in my backyard. I tried to think of the beauty in nature and how things take time, especially when you're trying to create a miracle.

So, my husband and I moved on to the "last" phase of our journey, IVF. But the bottom line is, the whole process is freaking hard. It's hard to think positively all the time, which is probably one of the main reasons why I can't stand hearing people say, "Just stay positive!" Or if someone tells you to "relax and don't stress." People, you have no idea. It's hard to regain all your strength and muster up the courage to try this all over again next month — and be "relaxed" about that. But I did it, because I couldn't give up — not yet anyway.

"The holiday season *amplifies* all emotions, and all anxieties related to *infertility*. It's really *freakin' hard.*"
—Me

The Holidays

My God, holidays suck when you're dealing with infertility. Yes, it's supposed to be a time of happiness and spending time with family and friends. However, those situations gave me anxiety. They brought on stress, worry, and depression. All I would think about would be my response to someone if they made a comment about pregnancy or babies. I absolutely love my family and being around them, especially the holidays or parties we have together. Going through infertility, though, and keeping it a secret from my family, was very difficult. I had a wall up to protect myself from the pain, even though I knew it would be inevitable if someone said even one thing about having another baby.

There were many occasions where a family member would say something to me. Deep down, I knew it wasn't to be malicious or cause me pain. I knew it was because they cared and wanted me to have that happiness. But it didn't feel that way at the time. Because I was struggling so much, any comment from anyone — from a loved one or a stranger — hurt me.

When I was in the middle of treatments and had been struggling for a year and a half, it made me even more stressed. I had very little hope and a lot of anger, so any comment could ruin my day. The holidays, or any gathering for that matter, were supposed to be about celebrations and catching up with each other. However, those were the conversations I would get so worked up over. I would worry about who would ask me a question or make a comment. I would mentally prepare for what I would say to people, days or weeks ahead of the event. I remember saying so many times, "Oh, we're so busy already, we can't handle anything else right now," or "Tyler has so much energy, he's enough for now!" Whatever stupid excuse I could think of, I would use.

I never had the guts to be blunt with anyone, even though the things people said to me were not okay. It just wasn't like me to be so forward and say what was really going on, probably because it hurt too much. Thinking back now, I should have stood up for myself and spoke up. I think that's what I'm trying to do by writing this: stand up for myself and for others so they don't have to go through all this alone.

The holidays were not exciting for me during this time — at all. It was really difficult to put on a smile and go to a gathering and pretend like everything was wonderful. Everyone was happy and feeling good; meanwhile, I was holding in this big secret and just trying to make it through without crying.

I felt like I was especially secretive during the holiday season. I think it's that way because it's a time when so many exciting life moments happen — people get engaged or announce they're pregnant. It's a special time, so you get excited and happy for each other and want to celebrate the milestones. However, when those milestones in your life are not happening, it's depressing. That's why the holidays sucked.

I once saw a post on Instagram about how December is the worst month for women with infertility. Why? Because it's freakin' Christmas. The time of miracles, the time baby Jesus was born. And here we are, no miracles happening, no babies on the way. It flat out hurts, really bad, and no one around you seems to understand, unless they're going through it themselves.

"Waiting the *10 days* after transfer to get my *blood taken* to see if I was pregnant was the *longest wait* of my life."

—Kelly, friend from high school

The Two-Week Wait

The two-week wait, or TWW, is the two week period between ovulation and your period. If you look up the phrase on Google, it will literally say — and I quote — "The two-week wait is a time of high anxiety, worry, and frustration for women trying to conceive."[1]

The longest two weeks of your life, legit. Sometimes it's so hard to stay positive during this time. All the thoughts going on in your head with every movement, twinge, pain, headache, pimple — could this mean I'm pregnant? Or could this just be early PMS? I would drive myself crazy thinking about if my body felt different or if I had any of these symptoms last month, or the countless months before that. And, if you're like me, I overthink anything and everything, so cue the stress, mood swings, attitude, emotions. It's a roller coaster 24/7.

Somehow, I've learned that I have to stay positive. It took a long time for me to get to that point. I had to dig deep, so deep, to keep it together for myself, my husband, and most importantly, my son.

In the beginning, worry would take over. It ate me up alive. I would be so sad or angry all the time. I would get upset at the smallest things and wonder what the hell was wrong with me. Why wasn't this working? It didn't take that long to conceive my son. I expected it would take longer, but I never, ever thought we would still be waiting almost two years later.

I felt like I'd done this cycle of waiting so many times that I was numb to it all. Pimples on my back? That happened before; doesn't mean anything. Feeling uncomfortable, like bloated except different? Been there, done that. I tried not to pay attention to any symptoms I had because I'd experienced it all, and it just got my hopes up. The breast tenderness, the breast pains (similar to the ones I got when I was pregnant with my son), mild cramps, acne — bad, like hormonal-teenager-bad — craving certain foods, then not wanting other food. Every single thing that I felt in my body, I always thought to myself, could this be it? But every time I was just let down.

I didn't want to tell my husband what was going on because then he would get his hopes up. That was the other heavy factor about the waiting game. There were two people that were holding on for dear life. Hanging on to any little shred of hope that we might have made a baby was everything to him. Every month when my period would come it would be like a tornado came through us and destroyed everything inside both of us, leaving us to pick up the pieces and rebuild what was left over. Month after month, that twister would leave less and less — of me, especially. How do you repair your belongings when you have so few things left? You have to find new resources. You have to work even harder. Even though you have to go to work every day, take care of your house, the laundry, pack lunches, take care of your sweet boy, and keep working on your marriage.

Yes, work on your marriage. It can be tough when you don't have serious issues, then you add this to the mix. It rips couples apart. This shit is hard — real hard. It's not just a physical thing; it's mental. So, so mental. The two-week wait is probably the part that plays with your head the most. Between second-guessing every change in your body and getting closer to the day you can take a test or going in for blood work, it really messes with you. The anxiety I would have walking up the hill to the door of RMA for that 6 am blood work to tell me if I was pregnant or not — wow. I can't even tell you. I swear it was like I couldn't get to that entrance fast enough. (Shoutout to the nurses who drew blood every morning at the crack of dawn at Basking Ridge, New Jersey, RMA. You would play music and have this positive energy about you that made me feel so good, even when I wasn't in the best of spirits. I am forever grateful for you and will never forget how great you made me feel through the hardest of days.).

Everything would weigh on that blood draw after two weeks. Whether it was just starting off with my treatments or IUI, that blood work was huge. Then after the blood work, I had to wait. It would be a few hours before I would get the call with positive or negative. Thinking about the calls now, I think about the nurse's side of things. That must be really hard for them, too. I guess that's the whole medical field, really. How do you not think about all your patients who are getting the short end of the stick in life? I know that as a teacher I think about my students all the time — how I can help them achieve their goals; how I can support them through their learning. I can't imagine how those nurses can make those phone calls every day, and make them with a kind and caring voice as well, even while I'm crying on the other end.

Thank you, nurses. I went through the "two-week wait," about 24 times. That's 24 months. Typing that doesn't seem like a lot, but it is. It's two years. Two years longer than I planned to have another baby. That's two weeks times 24, equaling 48 weeks of pure agony.

"I wanted it to be as fun and silly as possible to *distract you* from all of that worry and fear. So obviously, I grabbed a speaker, blasted *"Eye of the Tiger,"* and started dancing. And you immediately broke out *laughing and dancing* too, so I figured from that point on, I was going to get you *pumped up* to take those shots every time. And that's how *Simona's Superhero Playlist* got started!"
—Sonia

Music is Everything

I don't know what I would do without music in my life, especially during this time. If you take nothing from this book except for the sole fact that music will help get you through, then I'm fine with that.

For many of us, music makes us feel good, it gives us motivation and mental energy to push through whatever it is we're going through. It did just that for me, and more. Sure, certain songs made me cry, some made me angry, but some made me stronger. I think expressing and letting out all of those different emotions was part of the process for me. Music helped heal me. Words, melodies, beats — they all gave me life and purpose.

In those moments of agony and pain, I needed to put music on to get my mind off of things. Whether it was driving to work, or working in my craft room while my son napped, something would be playing. One song I would listen to over and over when I would get negative news was "Girl" by Maren Morris. It was the lyrics that really got to me. The words spoke to me directly. I would play it on my drive to work so many times, crying my eyes out, telling myself, "Everything's gonna be okay." I would try to tell myself that it would be okay no matter how my story ended. In those moments, even though I was crying, it helped me. It helped me move forward; it helped me let out the tears I'd been holding in for hours, days, weeks. Sometimes I'd sing along, if I had it in me, and just belt it out in my cracky, tear-filled voice.

Another one I recommend: Ellie Goulding, "Anything Could Happen." I mean, if it doesn't say enough in that title, I don't know what can. Just listen to it. It just makes you feel good, makes you think you can do this because you are so strong, anything could happen.

Music not only saved me each month after those dreaded phone calls, but through the whole process. What I mean is, the times when I would have to go for blood work or ultrasounds at the clinic, or do my injections each night, music would get me through. The times when I had to go to the office during monitoring hours, early in the morning before work — I'm talking 6 am — on my drive in, I'd play music by Taylor Swift, Maren Morris, Lady Gaga, Maroon 5, OneRepublic, or others that would pump me up.

Those drives became the regular for me, as did playing music. Once I would get into the blood work room, those ladies would have their own jams playing and, God, I loved them for that. I became familiar with their faces and names and would be comforted that it would be them doing blood work that morning. They'd play either reggae, hip hop, or other music that would just make you feel like smiling and getting this shit done.

I remember one day Aretha Franklin, "R-E-S-P-E-C-T" was playing and it just felt like it was going to be a good day. I thanked those ladies (and some men on occasion), but they never truly knew how much I sincerely appreciated them playing that background music to get me in the zone. Or how much I appreciated them just being so kind, or simply saying, "Have a blessed day, now." It made me feel so good. They made me feel like it was going to be okay no matter what. Thank you, to all of you wonderful ladies and gents, for being there at the crack of dawn and getting us into a good mood, even though that blood work didn't always bring us good things.

Rhythm, tempo, melody; all of the elements of music fueled me, especially when it came time to take out the needles. When I first started the shots, I would just play music in the background while I FaceTimed my mom or my sister. I guess I was trying to focus on what I was doing and it was all still new to me, so I was nervous. I should've known that playing the music closer to me and having that as my focus would relieve my stress and tension. Later on I learned to do that, and it helped me so much.

I'm talking girl-power, confident music to get me going. Bring on the Missy Elliott, Cardi B, Britney Spears, Rihanna, Normani, and then some! That helped amp me up to stick that needle in my stomach and forget about the pain I was about to endure. Yes, there was still pain, but I didn't think about it as much as when the music wasn't playing.

My sister really helped me when I had to increase my injections. I remember standing in my beach house kitchen with her; her laptop of playlists; my display of medications, needles, and an ice pack. The rest of my family was sitting just feet away in the living room, watching TV. We blasted the music and had a dance party throughout the entire thing. My sister would have "warm-up" songs to play as I would prepare the injection site, the needles, etc. Then she would have one or two "main songs" for when it was time to inject. These songs would be extra good. Hands down, Missy Elliott's "Work It" and "Lose Control" were some of the best. I wouldn't have even thought about creating a playlist for this if it wasn't for my sister (love you!). She planned and picked out all of our favorites and created "Simona's Superhero Playlist" on Spotify. I still listen to it. For one, because the songs are gold. Two, it reminds me of all that I went through and just how strong I am.

These songs helped me, not to move on, but to move forward. I hate the phrase, "Move on," because it makes me feel like I need to forget everything in my past. Like I can forget everything I did to get to this point! I think your past is what makes you stronger. Your struggles and your heartaches make you a more powerful you, if you're ready to let them. It's difficult to do, but, wow, can it really make a statement. I don't want to forget my past, as painful as it was. It shaped who I am today. It changed me, changed my husband, changed our family. With music, it helped us to move forward and appreciate what we have.

"I would *wake up* in the middle of the night with my mind *racing,* my anxiety through the roof, and feeling as if I had a watermelon in my uterus from being *so bloated* … Feeling like your body *isn't working* "as it should be" can create more and more of a *negative spiral.*"
—Vicki

My Body

Let me start with saying that women's bodies are incredible. The things we are made to achieve and what we endure is unbelievable. We truly are warriors. But let me back up a minute because I certainly didn't feel this way all the freakin' time. There were times when I hated my body for the things it could, but mostly could not, do.

For example, how is it possible for my body to keep bleeding for seven days? That's right, seven days, not three or four or even five days. My period lasted that long for it to be completely gone. You'd think that this would be a time when God would cut me some slack, but no. It didn't matter that I'd hated the sight of seeing that first drop of blood every damn month, but then it had to continue for a week.

We all know what comes with that lovely monthly delivery — hormones, mood swings, headaches, cramps, food cravings; the whole nine yards. This made it so incredibly easy to want to do my daily life routines — *not*. It also made my roller coaster of weight really fun. I'd go down, then up, then steady. When I would step on the scale and I was close to getting my period and I saw the number go up — I just knew. I knew it wasn't going to be this month.

Within the first year of trying to conceive naturally, my weight was pretty much the same. Sure, I was still holding on to a few extra pounds from when I had my son, but nothing crazy. I was content with how I looked. I was exercising more by this time too. My husband had taken on a love of running, which had a ripple effect on me and I really got into it. I would always walk or jog on the treadmill, but I had grown a love for running too. It was a way to relieve my stress after a long day at work or a rough day home with my toddler. I looked forward to that 30–45 minute period of focusing on me and getting in shape. I would either listen to dance music to get me going, watch a show on Netflix, or catch up on a good book I was into at the time. Either way, it was a de-stressor and it was something I looked forward to.

Once I started going to RMA and began infertility treatments, I started to have restrictions on things. I couldn't drink alcohol while I was on certain medications; couldn't run or do intensive workouts. The reason was that certain meds would enlarge my ovaries, so if I ran or did high intensity workouts, I ran the risk of ovarian torsion (twisting your ovaries), which is extremely painful and dangerous. I was nervous to even jog while on those meds. This wouldn't be all the time, but once I got to the second and third phases it was pretty permanent that I could only walk as a form of exercise. Yes, I know that's better than nothing, but it wasn't the same as running. I felt exhilarated and empowered when I ran.

At this time, it was the end of May in 2019 and my family and I would always go to the beach. We are lucky enough to own a beach house with my in-laws, so once the warm weather starts you can find us there pretty much every weekend, although even that had its ups and downs for me while I was going through this. I wasn't in the best mental state and I didn't really want to be around people all the time.

On the flip side, my in-laws were awesome and watched Tyler so that my husband and I could go out. We would go to a bar on the boardwalk with live music and just get away for an hour or two. This was a great oasis some days. Other days — when I wasn't allowed to drink alcohol — it sucked. Sure, let me get a virgin Bloody Mary or a stupid tonic and cranberry — that was exciting.

I think I was so mad about it because I didn't think any of this would work. Deep down, I was hoping and praying that this would all be worth it. Then, it was June — nothing. Next, it was July — nothing. Then came August, and you guessed it: nothing. These months were supposed to be stress-free, relaxing, rejuvenating to get back on track for the new school year, but there was none of that for me.

Those beautiful beach days, I tried my hardest to relax, but all I could think about was how I couldn't make a baby, I couldn't run, and I couldn't drink. I thought I would be better, but I was just as miserable. To have two major outlets taken away was much harder than I thought. I would look at my body every morning and see it changing before my eyes. I watched myself put on pound after pound. I would look at my growing, bloated belly and wonder if it would ever get back to what it used to be.

Sure, you could tell me to watch what I ate, and for the most part I did! However, when you're restricted from two stress-relievers like exercise and alcohol, it's very difficult to stay in the right frame of mind to also be on a strict diet. Each day I was trying my hardest to stay positive, but when you have all this build-up weighing on your shoulders and nowhere to let it go, you eat. You indulge yourself sometimes, or maybe more than sometimes (especially when it's summer and you have Kohr's Ice Cream at your fingertips). And guess what? That's okay.

Throughout the summer, this was my mental state. It was a

constant struggle of wanting to get in shape but not being able to push myself to get there. Summertime is when everyone lets loose, enjoys cocktails and parties, and enjoys life in general. I tried so, so hard to be that way, but I couldn't bring myself to be there all the time. Infertility really fucks with your mind in ways you never imagined. It also screws up your body, physically.

Maybe you're one of the lucky ones whose body can handle anything and heals quickly. Me, I've never been that way. I've always been like a banana: you smack me on the arm joking around — bruise. Playing lacrosse in high school, I barely got hit — bruises. If I bumped into the corner of the bed, my God, I'd be bruised for weeks. So, at 32 and 33 years old, it was still the same, if not worse, and I had to go inject myself with needles.

I friggin' hate needles. The first phase of treatments was when I would do "trigger shots." The next phase was more intense medications by injections, in addition to the trigger shots. Lots and lots of shots. These were all going into my stomach. Of course, the beginning was the hardest, but it never got easier. I just got used to it.

As I said about the bruising, it began instantly. Not every shot gave me a bruise — sometimes I just got red and a little swollen. It sucked, no matter how my body reacted. It was a constant reminder of the torture and pain I was going through. Some days, while I was teaching, I'd forget for a split second and then when I sat down, my pants would rub against the bruises and bring it all back to me.

At night when I would shower, I'd look in the mirror at my stomach. I could see every shot I injected into my belly because it would always leave a mark, whether it was a small red dot or a massive blue and purple bruise. It hurt to look at myself in the mirror. It would bring on this wave of sadness, anger and frustration. I'd stare at myself for a few minutes and then huff and go about my business.

Sometimes it felt as if I was just going through the motions. I'd do what the doctor and nurse's orders were that day/week/ month and hope for the best, but I'll tell you right now, I wasn't very hopeful or happy about it. It all took a toll on me. Night after night it was shots, bruising, crying, and a state of feeling nothing at the same time. Each night when it was time to get started (because the shots had to be in a certain time frame), I'd call my mom or my sister to FaceTime while I did it. My husband couldn't watch because he'd get sick (literally).

Did I absolutely need someone there? Probably not, but it made me feel better that "someone" was watching my steps and making sure I did it right. There were videos and everything about how exactly to do it. I would have my laptop set up next to me playing the video and my phone propped up right next to it for FaceTime. The other tricky part was that I had to do the shots about an inch away from each other and could not inject into the same injection site from the previous night. That became difficult and left very little space after doing it seven or eight nights in a row.

I remember one night I had a very small spot that was clear for me to do my shot, but I had to be careful because I had a huge bruise next to it from a few nights ago and another injection site on the other side. Now, I forgot to mention, I try my best to watch the needle go into my skin, but sometimes I just stab it in and don't watch the whole thing (the needles weren't always very short). This particular night, I was a hair off from my targeted spot. I injected the needle right into my bruise.

When I tell you the pain was excruciating, it doesn't do it justice. It was gushing blood, I fell to my knees crying in pain, but I didn't understand why. When I looked down, I saw I had hit the bruise.

Infertility fucking sucks. Shots suck. The struggle sucks. The pain sucks. The physical and mental states your body endures suck.

When it came time for IVF, the final phase of fertility treatments, it was a whole other ball game of meds and protocols. This was the real deal, in my mind. Maybe that's what I thought all along and maybe that's why I kept getting negative test after negative test. (This is where my mind goes.)

There were more steps for IVF. I had to first do the retrieval. This process was somewhat like the other phases, where I would give myself injections to grow my eggs and get them ready to be taken out. This was when I was taking three shots in one night in my stomach. Again, I could not exercise like I wanted to for the risk of twisting my ovaries. I was allowed to walk, but at this point I was just too scared to do anything and take the chance of something bad happening.

That's really how I felt once it was time for IVF. I thought that this was it; if it didn't work and I was exercising I would think that was the reason it didn't work. So, I cut it all out and hoped for the best.

The retrieval went better than anticipated, thankfully. And after that procedure, I rested. There were a few weeks in between before they just planted those beautiful embryos in my uterus. It was the waiting game. Waiting for results; waiting to know if my eggs made it to that golden stage. No, this may not have weighed on my body physically, but it did emotionally. That's still a part of your body and it still affects you, mentally. Which, really, can be more important than your physical appearance. That time period of about a week was probably one of the most anxious and stressful times. Every month of waiting was stressful, but this was different. We knew that if we didn't get any embryos, this would change everything. It would mean doing another retrieval or possibly stopping completely.

When I got the call from my nurse saying that three embryos made it to the blastocyst stage, I started to tear up and chills ran through my body. When I called my husband, I could hear it in his voice — the sigh of relief, the "it's all going to be okay" feeling. I felt so good knowing we had three chances at this. Deep down in my gut, I knew it would be okay. My head wasn't fully convinced, probably because it knew a tough road still lay ahead, but we took the good news and let that sink in for a while.

The next step was our transfer. I told you this was a long process — nothing like the rest. For the transfer, I had to take estrogen pills three times a day and start progesterone shots once a day in my upper buttocks region.

Queue my husband stepping up his game. He got up to the plate and nailed it out of the park. He did great giving me my shots every morning. I was happy I didn't have to do it myself because, mentally, that was a lot to handle and I stressed about it every night when I had to do them in the past.

It still hurt, of course, and I had to alternate left and right cheeks to even it all out. There was a trick too — don't sit or lay down afterward because it could sit there and bubble up. This was progesterone in oil, so moving around helped it flow (according to my nurse). And along this great journey, I learned to ice the area before I did the injection for less bruising and a little less pain. Unfortunately, I still bruised at times, but the ice helped me to bruise less.

We did that every morning at 6:40 am before my husband

left for work, while my son would watch TV or play games. We got it down to a routine, and each day it was the norm for us.

The progesterone shots started before the official transfer and continued after the transfer as well. They were supposed to help prepare my body for a pregnancy; to help my body produce progesterone until my body did so naturally. We did our first transfer and from that moment on, the nurses told me to act as if I was pregnant. Since I had the embryo transferred to my uterus, it basically was as if I was carrying a child.

So, I did just that. I watched what I ate and drank and acted as if I was pregnant until it was time for the pregnancy test two weeks later. Of course, with my luck, the first time didn't work. I remember getting that call. It wasn't my nurse that called, it was my doctor, but I didn't expect that something was wrong. I was in my craft room at the time and my doc just kept talking, but I couldn't hear anything after he said, "I'm sorry, I'm afraid I don't have good news." I remember calling my husband upstairs to have my doctor repeat everything he said to me again. He wasn't sure why it didn't work. It could've been that it just wasn't a good embryo. My mind was blown. I could tell my husband felt defeated too. We had lost our embryo. We had lost our embaby. The little hope and excitement I had in me, thinking I may be really pregnant, was gone.

I don't think I actually processed losing that embryo until after having my daughter. That was a big deal, but I never took the time to mourn. I was sad and upset, of course, but I saw it as just another treatment that didn't work. It was a loss. I know that now, after being a part of the infertility community. I see that this was something serious and terrible. I think at the time though, in my head, I just thought, "Keep going, keep pushing forward, you're almost there." I had to get through the next steps and try everything. I wish I had slowed down a bit and gave myself the time to just breathe and think about what my body had just gone through.

We went back up the roller coaster again. I could hear the *tick-tick* as the car got higher and higher. I could feel the roller coaster getting weaker and weaker each month we had a failure. I could feel it in my bones that I only had a few more chances left in me before I couldn't do this anymore. I knew we had two more embryos, so that would be it for me. My husband and I discussed and agreed that we couldn't do this much longer. I thought to myself after processing this, how could I have been so dumb to think this would work on the first try? As I thought about next steps, I made sure I was hopeful, but also prepared myself for the reality that it might not work.

We went on to do our second transfer. This time, we didn't tell anyone about the details. It was too much; too much repeating myself about what was going on; too much of the well wishes and "stay positive" stuff; too much for me to handle. We kept it just to ourselves. Two days before Christmas, I hoped that maybe some of that holiday magic would help us. Being on break from school was also a big relief. I didn't have to worry about teaching or running around. My body could truly just rest.

After the transfer, I really made sure to do absolutely nothing, except rest. I remember my husband even took our son to play golf on Christmas Eve to give me a break. I usually hosted that night and had my in-laws and friends over for a nice dinner, but we pushed it back until after the holidays. That's how serious I was about giving my body all the rest it could get. I needed to do this, to know that I had done everything I possibly could to give my body what it needed to help make this pregnancy happen. Sure, it was hard to change that big Christmas Eve dinner without giving many details, but everyone understood without the need to hear exactly why.

I don't know if it was the rest I gave myself, if it was "the right embryo," if God and Santa worked their magic, or if it was just our time, but it worked.

It freakin' worked.

I didn't think it would, but I was hoping, praying, and begging on every little thing and it goddamn worked. Thank you, Jesus; thank you, Santa; and thank you, Science.

Since being pregnant, I still cringe at the sight of my rolls in the mirror. Yeah, yeah, I know that's so vain and I shouldn't worry about that, but I do. I think that's what it is: I worry about the weight. I worry about having to tack that on my to-do list. With my first child, I gained about 60 pounds; no joke. I honestly could not tell you how, either. My husband and I are not poor eaters. I mean, we would indulge now and then, but nothing crazy. I wondered how I put on so much weight, and then at one of my doctor appointments they had told me I had excess amniotic fluid, which added to the weight. My son was also an eight-pounder, so there's that. Then, I did not have the best labor and delivery. They pumped me full of fluids and drugs. I think I gained more weight while I was in the hospital! But in the end, I was able to lose the weight — all but 5–10 pounds.

When I looked in the mirror this time and saw at the beginning of my pregnancy that I already had the extra weight, I worried even more. Would I gain more weight this time? Less? Would I also have the excess amniotic fluid problem or other complications? Would I be able to have a healthy pregnancy, labor, and delivery?

The questions never go away. A year into treatments, I was the heaviest I'd ever been, besides when I was pregnant with Tyler. I know why though. I hadn't been able to truly exercise for seven months.

Seven months.

Sure, I walked on the treadmill or went for short walks here and there. Whenever there was a time that I was off the medications (after a failed month), I'd go run on the treadmill or go for a long walk outside. But those chances were few and far between. With that restriction and being on so many different medications for almost a year, I put on weight. About 10 pounds, to be exact. That's a lot, especially when I hadn't fully lost the baby weight from my son. Some people might think it's no big deal, but when your clothes start getting tighter and tighter (and still no baby), it messes with your head.

When I wrote this, I was only seven weeks pregnant. I was scrambling for clothes that fit me in the morning; not to mention clothes that looked appropriate for work but also didn't show my belly because I didn't want people asking questions. Talk about complicated. Inside, I was excited yet cautious. I was planning out every part of my outfit, checking it twice in the mirror. I knew if I showed just a little bit of a bulge of my belly, people would wonder if I was pregnant. I wasn't ready for that, it was too soon. I could see the light at the end of the tunnel, I was yearning for it, but I wasn't there yet.

I hadn't reached the safe point yet, so I had to keep going in secrecy.

"I didn't start *sharing* my story actively with acquaintances, fellow colleagues, other friends, or even openly on social media *until 2018*. I felt like God had/has a *bigger purpose* for our journey and part of that, in my opinion, is being open and making the topic of infertility *less taboo*. I have received such beautiful messages and words of support and encouragement since *opening up*."

—Vicki

Opening Up

It's hard to be in that little bubble by yourself, thinking about a secret every single time you're with your family, friends, coworkers, or even strangers. The reason it's so hard is because those people will talk about the very thing you've been keeping hidden and they'll have opinions about it — good or bad. It makes you think a lot. It sometimes makes you feel less likely to share what you've been keeping safe in your heart for so long.

I kept my struggle with infertility from my entire family (and everyone I know) for a long time. If you're anything like me, I felt ashamed, embarrassed and I just didn't want to open myself up to any questions or comments. It was so hard to keep that secret inside of me, especially when family members would somehow bring it up in conversation.

"Do you think you'll have another one?"

"Make sure you don't wait too long because you want to have them close in age!"

"You need to have a girl."

It was hard. There's no other way to say it. This is a hard thing to handle by itself. Sharing it with more and more people meant that I would hear more "I'm sorry's," "We're here for you," "We'll keep praying," "Stay positive." I wasn't ready for all of that.

I can't remember when I first told my sister, but she was the first one to tell because we're very close. Then, once things got more serious and I had to go through my hysterosalpingography (HSG) — an x-ray to show whether the fallopian tubes are blocked or not — blood work, and then referral to RMA, I knew I had to tell my parents what was going on.

It was all too much, but I just stuck to the facts of everything. I'm usually an emotional person, but I couldn't get all worked up. My mom didn't pry. She just listened and stayed positive, which is all I wanted, really. I did the same with my dad and he was good about it too. He asked more questions than I anticipated, but it was fine to talk about it. But that was it. I didn't expand to my cousins, aunts, or uncles just yet. I knew my family would be there for me no matter what and would support me, but I also knew it was a very large family with lots of comments and opinions — not that they would necessarily say them to my face, but in my head I thought about that. Like I said, I was not thinking clearly, let alone positively. I chose to hold off on telling them for a while.

For almost a year, only our parents and siblings knew. I had also told my friend, Stacey, who I worked with. She taught first grade and I taught second. We were right across the hall from each other. I needed her more than I even knew. I had some really tough days; days when I thought I wouldn't be able to move forward and she would be there to help lift me back up and get me back on the wagon. She knew about pretty much everything I was going through. I could trust her with my life.

I finally did tell my extended family right before starting IVF for the first time. It was a long-winded, time-consuming process. I think that, after having the most difficult, energy-draining, stress-inducing class of my life the past year and dealing with infertility and all the emotions it brings, I hadn't realized what might be happening inside me. I knew it was affecting me, but I don't think I fully understood just how much until summer came. It was the end of August of 2019 when I finally opened up to my family and friends. We have a family group chat, so that was the best way to do it all at once. I guess I didn't realize the magnitude of the support and love I'd get back. It was amazing and too much all at the same time. I always knew my family would be there for me, but I didn't think about how emotional it would be for me to share our struggle with them.

I remember I was making dinner after I sent out that text message and then my phone just kept on buzzing from return messages. I was in tears; tears of joy because everyone was so nice, but also tears of sadness because I couldn't bring another baby into this world, into this family. It was a bittersweet moment. I felt relieved to let my secret out for sure, but I still had that feeling of sadness. I knew this was part of my healing process, though; to share the secret that I'd been hiding. Even though it may have been difficult to open up, it was another step forward that I had to take.

The last step (and probably the least important) was posting on social media. This was big, but not as big as opening up to my family. This was sharing the news to friends and others on social media because, again, it was part of the process. It was also about raising awareness. That was the main reason I wanted to post. Seeing all these brave women post about every step of their infertility journey was amazing to me. I felt empowered by them and supported, so I wanted to do the same and hopefully help those who were watching and holding onto secrets as well.

Just like posting, writing this book was a part of my healing process. I want to continue to make this the norm. I want to continue to talk about every single part of this — the good, the bad and the ugly. Life is rarely perfect, so let's be real and support each other.

"I learned how *resilient* I am. I don't even know if I knew what resilience and strength were before this *chapter in my life.* I learned that my worth as a *woman* is still present even if I am not a mother yet. I now *understand* that having a master plan for my life is not in my control. Instead, life should be looked at as an *opportunity* to *'go with the flow.'*"

—Vicki

Moving Forward

There will always be that part of me that will sting a little when I hear someone else is pregnant, when I see a pregnant woman, when I see a newborn baby, or even a family with several children. My mind even makes me wonder how each family was made. Did they do IVF? Did they adopt? Did they struggle to have that only child? And sometimes I'll have those negative thoughts like, "It must be nice to have created those babies without any suffering or sacrifice," or "How is that fair, God, that someone else who doesn't even want a child can get pregnant by accident?!"

So many thoughts run through my head. I assume it's natural for someone who has gone through what I have. We question how life happens for some and not others; we wonder why.

I do continue to live by "Everything happens for a reason," though. I've stuck by that quote since before I can remember; probably when I was in middle school and my hormones (and everyone else's) started to kick in. I just remember telling myself that it was happening for a reason and I had to get through it. So that's what I would eventually come around to after each month of failure: there was a reason for it. Even though it freakin' sucked and I hated that that was the outcome, I knew I'd move forward. Some days, I didn't know how I'd keep going, but I did. I did for my husband, I did for my son. I knew I should keep going for myself, and some days I did, but others I just couldn't.

Along this journey, I've learned to take time for myself. I realized that I needed to do more self-care. This was in the middle of all this chaos, when my class was extremely difficult and stressful and I was beginning fertility drugs. I felt like I was drowning, but I was trying my darndest to just stay above water. Reading good books, following positive role models on social media, and, of course, watching Ellen on DVR were just some of the ways I tried to stay on track.

Self-care doesn't necessarily mean going out for massages, getting my nails done all the time, spa days, or extremely elaborate and expensive things. Sure, I would love to do those things on a regular basis, but that just wasn't practical for me while working full-time, taking care of my son, etc. I had to focus on things that brought me joy that I could do for an hour before my day started or after everyone was asleep. Just an hour or so to myself to do something that I really enjoyed. I needed that each and every day.

Most days I would watch Ellen at night after my son would go to sleep. It would be just what I needed — laughter or tears of joy. I needed to remember that there was good in the world, but more importantly, that I was lucky to have what I had in my life because many days I would forget that. Then I got on a kick of waking up early, around 5 am, and got my butt on the treadmill for at least a half hour. It felt so good to do that. I'm not a morning person, but I felt energized and happy to start my day that way. After my workout, I still had time before everyone woke up, so I would have a nice cup of coffee while I either checked my email or read a book.

A few books in particular that were great to read during this time were *This Is Me* by Chrissy Metz, *Infreakinfertility* by Melanie Dale, and *Dear Girls* by Ali Wong.

Another recommendation to help keep you going is to find some good podcasts. It really helped me focus on the bigger picture of things, focus on my goals, and reminded me that I'm good enough. I really enjoyed listening to *WHOA that's Good* with Sadie Robertson (from the Duck Dynasty family). I would listen to it on the way to work or on the way home, or sometimes while I would craft. It made me feel empowered when I felt weak and alone.

If you noticed, all the authors I mentioned are women. I needed the girl power. I needed the inspiration to move forward because most days my energy was very low. I had barely anything left to give, especially in the spring. I was in the beginning phases of fertility drugs and blood work and the whole nine yards. Throw in anxious students ready for spring break and the end of the school year approaching and they wouldn't listen for anything. I was shot, to say the least. Especially when month after month of fertility drugs resulted in no baby.

Like I said, I tried. I tried really hard every single day. But it was so difficult to give all I had to my work, my family, and my friends. I think part of the time, my body was just going through the motions and my mind and soul were somewhere else. I can't explain to you how much the pain dug down deep. I was in a dark, dark place and I was not nice half the time — I'll admit that. I'm not making excuses for myself, but listen, anyone who has gone through this or knows someone who has may understand just a little bit.

As I was reading *Dear Girls*, I wasn't expecting to read about serious moments. I was surprised when I got to chapter two and she told her readers that she had a miscarriage. I instantly felt her pain. I haven't experienced a miscarriage, but I've experienced month after month of failure and one unsuccessful IVF transfer (loss of embryo), which was a major loss. I watched those doctors place that embryo in my uterus and I posted that picture of my baby as a little blob on my fridge. I told my immediate family about it and showed them "my embryo baby." I thought in my head, "I'm pregnant, this is it." I stayed positive. I did all the things my doctors and nurses told me to do.

Then of course, there I was in my craft room and I saw the "No Caller ID" pop up on my phone. I instantly had a pit in my stomach. I knew who that could be: either my therapist — and I wasn't expecting a call from her — or my doctor.

It was rare for my doctor to call me. Sometimes, since the beginning of this process, he'd call to just ask how I was doing, but mostly he called to give me serious news. The last time he called, it was to tell me my insurance wouldn't cover IVF unless I did another round of IUI.

I picked up the phone and he gave me the bad news before I thought to get my husband in the room. I couldn't process it. I just thought to myself — why? How is this possible? I saw that embryo go in. I just thought, "What was it that I did that this didn't work again?"

Our doctor explained all the details and percentages and I understood, I guess. It didn't make it any easier, of course, but I appreciated him calling to give us the news. So there we were, on the high of hoping and praying we were having a baby only to be told, "The embryo didn't make it. It wasn't the right one."

I was crushed. I went on my typical binge of a three-day-ish depression. It was something I had to do. I had to mourn, I had to grieve, I had to question every little move I made in the last few weeks to see what had caused this. I would usually blame myself for those days and try to figure out what I could do better the next month. I would cry hard the first day. The next day would be much less, but I would cry or crack at the most random things. By day three, I was pretty much numb, frustrated, and in a state of hopelessness. I just wanted to get out of this merry-go-round, but I couldn't get off of it.

By day four or five, I would push all those feelings way down inside of me and move on to whatever it was I had to do. In this case, it was to try again. Of course, I thought that if my body rejected it once, how could it possibly work the second time around? I knew, though, that I had two more chances, since I had two more embryos. I told myself over and over, "After this is done, I will get my body and my life back to where I want it to be."

As hard as it was during those "valleys," I kept going. Somehow, some way, I did. It may not have been with a smile on my face, but I pushed through. Brené Brown stated in an interview with *The Today Show*:

"I've never seen a single person who has built a life, a family or a career that did not have to scratch their way up from a fall and begin again a hundred times. What starts here changes the world, but it will not be on your terms and it will not be on your timeline. The world will not ready itself for our plans. What starts here will change the world, but it will take your commitment to get back up and begin again the exact same number of times you fall, trip or get pushed down."[1]

Wow. It was like Brené was talking directly to me. I know this has been said in other ways by other people, but I think it's important to hear it over and over again, especially in times of despair. I feel like this statement burns a fire under my ass. It gives me motivation to keep working towards whatever goal it is that I have my mind set on. Life may take you on other paths that you may not have expected, but where you land may be exactly where you need to be. Just keep moving forward, whatever that may look like for you.

"Do not let *infertility* take over your life. It very easily can, because of *endless appointments,* shots, etc., but continuing to have *hobbies* and exercising helps to keep your mind *busy.*"
—Katie, friend from work

This Was It

It was June of 2019. The school year was finishing up. I thought that by having nothing to worry about except my son, that I would feel so good. I'd be relaxed, at ease, primed to make that baby. It was going to happen this summer and I would plan my maternity leave perfectly, just like I did with Tyler.

Well, June came and went and when it was time for my period to come, it showed up like it always did. So I drank. I drank when I could. It was my way of saying to myself, "Fuck this." Then it got to the point when I couldn't drink, like, at all. My medications didn't allow me to drink, or if I did have one glass I was told I'd have to drink even more water because I'd get very dehydrated.

The main side effect of my medications was dehydration. I'm already a big water drinker, but I needed to add more to my day. For example, I would drink about 75–80oz of water normally and now my average is 96–120oz. I knew it was affecting my body when my hands would be so dry in the middle of the summer that I would have cuts on my palms. So, to me, drinking alcohol wasn't worth it.

After the year I had with my class, then being a month into summer and not being able to drink or run — it took a bit of a toll on me. I grew to love running and I would do it regularly.

It was my stress reliever. It made me feel good, physically and mentally. After I completed a run I felt accomplished. I felt great inside and out. Not being able to run was tougher than I thought. At first, I said to myself, "It's fine, I can just do long walks or speed walks. It'll be fine."

"Fine," I said. Yeah right. It wasn't the same thing. I loved those runs on the boardwalk and now I had to walk. I adjusted, but I wasn't satisfied. I was still mad and stressed out over things that were being stripped away from me. I was pushing back on those limitations instead of letting go and staying positive.

I thought the summer would be my time. I thought that since I wasn't working I'd be less stressed and more at ease, which would relax my body. Well, I was so wrong. At the end of August of 2019, I was preparing for the new school year. I had just done my first cycle of IUI and it had failed. I knew deep down that it wasn't going to work the next time, so I asked my nurse if I could go straight to IVF and her and my doctor had agreed. They agreed that I had tried everything (every phase, at least twice) and we would move forward to the IVF cycle.

I started my birth control cycle for the 7–10 days while insurance was processed (always the time-sucker). I thought I'd be going to start my meds for the beginning of IVF and get my retrieval done before school started so I wouldn't have to worry about taking time off, worrying about the pain, etc. However, it didn't work out in my favor yet again. My doctor called me and I knew that something was up. He told me that my insurance wouldn't cover the IVF cycle if I didn't do at least two rounds of IUI.

I was blown away. I hadn't expected this at all. I was so frustrated, sad, and torn apart that I wanted to scream. I did scream. I even said straight to my doctor, "This really sucks." I didn't understand how insurance could dictate my life. It threw my whole plan out of whack. My doctor said he spoke with the insurance company himself to try to explain, but they still wouldn't do it. Hearing that, I knew I had no other option but to do what they said. I pushed forward with this new plan, one I hadn't anticipated and one I didn't like. It was more time, more money, more of the stuff that wasn't enjoyable.

Later that week, I was driving to Connecticut for a family event. I went by myself and left Tyler with my husband for the weekend and just drove while listening to music. That time was exactly what I needed. Space to breathe, space to think. As I was a bit into my drive, I just listened and let my thoughts go.

Now this next thing I'm going to tell you, you either believe or you don't. I can't describe what I was feeling other than it was this huge wave of release over my entire body. It felt like a rush of air just got sucked out of me, like it took away my anger and angst. I felt more at peace, more at ease, than I have in a long, long time. In that moment I thought to myself, "It's okay, it's all going to be okay... I'm done living a secret."

"At the time, we were *unable to afford* treatments because we did not have *fertility benefits* through our insurance."
—Vicki

Insurance

Ugh, insurance. It can be a blessing and it can also be a curse. I've had my share of both. I'll say it right off the bat: I know my experience is not the worst. Since I'm a teacher, I know we have pretty good insurance, and I'm grateful for that. Each clinic or doctor visit, I only had to pay copays of about $10 once I hit my insurance deductible. That was just the fee for visiting the doctor, though. Then came the medications, which I still had to pay a decent amount for. My insurance would pay a percentage and I would pay the remainder, so I knew I could have had it worse.

I guess I realized how lucky I was when, one time, I was checking in at RMA and I was about to pay my copay and I overheard a woman next to me paying $40 for her regular blood work and ultrasound visit. Those were the main types of visits I had every time I was there; sometimes just blood work and other times both. Copays alone of $40 each time is a lot of money — and that's just the visits, never mind the medications and procedures you go through.

One thing that drove me nuts about my insurance, though, was that they basically dictated what I could and could not do. For example, at the end of the summer of 2019, I had done one round of IUI, which had failed. I was so upset because I knew it wasn't going to work if we tried a second time. I spoke with my doctors and nurses about moving straight to IVF instead of do-

ing another IUI round. They were on board and recommended it.
We started preparing for that cycle. I had started taking the birth
control pills and other medications to prepare.

Then I got the call from my doctor directly, about a week
or two later. I remember exactly where I was when he called. I
was in my car driving home with my son in the backseat. I don't
remember where I had gone that day or what I had done before
that phone call, but I remember talking to him at a stop sign just
frozen in time as I listened to what he was telling me.

I wanted to call up my insurance and give them a piece of my
goddamn mind. They refused to pay anything for my IVF cycle.
I was shocked. The catch was I had to do another round of IUI
before they would cover anything for IVF. My insurance policy
would cover a majority of my costs, but I had to do two rounds
of everything before moving on to the next, which was why I
did two rounds of each phase. This was bullshit. How does an
insurance company get to dictate my life, or anyone else's for that
matter? How do they get to fuck with my fertility?

I know my doctor fought so hard to get them to approve it,
but it wasn't happening. This was the beginning of rock-bottom
for me. It had derailed all of my plans to get pregnant before the
school year started. I had it all laid out in my mind: IUI would
work and I'd be pregnant and go on maternity leave the second
half of the school year and start fresh the following year.

Nope. Insurance crushed my dreams of no more stress.

Another bump in the road came along later: my insurance
was possibly going to change. I couldn't believe it. I remember
sitting in my union meeting hearing the news. I started freaking
out. My insurance was going to be different. It was going to
change to something that I wasn't familiar with. Copays could
be different, procedures could be different. I was literally having

a panic attack there and then in my head. But I couldn't say anything without people asking questions or wondering what the heck was wrong with me. I had to take a deep breath and try and process what obstacles would lie ahead for me. I mean, I wasn't only seeing a gynecologist. I was seeing specialists and therapists. To think that the process could change and cost more money... I was really panicking, to say the least.

Thankfully, our insurance did not change. I didn't have to deal with that on top of everything else. Even with that said, I know I'm still lucky. After finding an infertility community online and talking with more people, I learned over time that I had it good. I heard from some women that their insurance would only cover if they did *five* rounds of IUI! What the actual hell? I mean, time is of the essence here! Don't they know this?! I know there is still a chance after a few rounds of the same method, but I was one to think that if it's not working, move on to the next. It just made me so angry to know that this was how our healthcare system worked. Not okay.

Again, I will say I am very lucky to have the majority of my medications and procedures covered. I know I can't complain much, but I can complain a little. And then I can complain *a lot* on other people's behalf! This is not fair. There are so many people whose health insurance doesn't cover anything for fertility treatments and they pay everything out of pocket. This process is stressful in and of itself. Add the pressures of the financial burden and it's a recipe for disaster.

I remember sitting in the gorgeous waiting room of the Basking Ridge office of RMA one morning (when they were really backed up) and a woman was so upset. She had been waiting so long that she was going to be late for work. She was so emotional and upset (and I couldn't blame her) that she went off at the poor receptionists about how she's spent over $40,000 already and that she shouldn't be waiting... and she went on.

I felt bad. I felt bad for the receptionists because it wasn't their fault it was an off day (there was rarely a wait at 6 am). I felt bad for the people around the room listening and waiting too. And I felt bad for that poor woman. I could feel her pain. We just wanted one thing so badly and we spent money, time, and energy just to be stressed out and pushed to our very limits. I hope that woman got her baby and is happy now, wherever she is.

Infertility is a disease. It's a problem for so many women — and men. You can go Google infertility right now and get statistics on it. According to the World Health Organization (WHO), "it can be primary or secondary and estimates suggest that between 48 million couples and 186 million individuals live with infertility globally" (WHO).[1] One in eight people suffer from infertility. Fertility experts agree that, on average, 30 percent of the cases of infertility they see can be attributed solely to the female, 30 percent solely to the male, 30 percent a combination of both partners, and in 10 percent of cases the cause is unknown (which is the case for my husband and I).[2]

This needs to be discussed. It needs to be part of our health insurance, because this is not a minor thing.

"I don't know exactly what my *expectations* were going into *IVF,* but I don't think I was prepared to hear that our first try *didn't take.* But, I got up, brushed off my pants and was ready for *round two.*"
—Kelly

The IVF Cycle

I want to preface this with: I was really hoping I wouldn't have to get to this step. I was praying so hard and thinking all the good thoughts to help get myself pregnant. I knew IVF had a higher success rate than all the other fertility treatments I had tried; however, it scared the crap out of me. I knew it was a lot more involved. More injections, a lot more medications, and many more trips to the office to be monitored. It made me anxious to think about everything extra that I would have to do when I was already stressing about doing my one injection a night the past few months. But I also knew that if I didn't go through with this and at least try, I would regret it for the rest of my life.

When it was time to get monitored during the birth control period (yes, totally backwards with what we're trying to achieve here, but it helps to control your body to not grow and release any eggs/follicles until it is time), my lovely body decided to rebel against the birth control and grow one anyway. When I went in thinking I was going to start my meds and get this baby process really started, I got the lovely news that I had a cyst. The doctor said it was a cyst/follicle.

What the hell? It was another possible chance, or at least that's what I thought in my mind. A possibility that my body could get pregnant without the rest of the in vitro process. So, of course, I had to take an injection to release the cyst/follicle and I had specific orders from my nurse to have wine and intercourse that night.

No problem! There I went on that emotional high, thinking, "This could be it, it's a miracle my body did this — God, I hear you!" I got excited. I got hopeful again. I thought, "Oh my gosh, I won't have to go through IVF."

Well, of course, I got my period a couple weeks later and the cyst had disappeared. I was on to the last phase of science: in vitro fertilization.

The start of my cycle for IVF meant I had to get my body ready for the retrieval. If you don't know what that is, it's literally the retrieval of all of the eggs that grow in your ovaries. In order to grow as many as possible, I had to begin hormonal drugs to get my body to make them.

I was used to giving myself one shot a night and that was hard enough. However, for this step, it started off with one shot for a few nights, then two shots, and then up to three in one night. I had to do three shots per night for about a week or so.

My sister — oh, my God — when I tell you that my sister saved me, she truly did. I could not have done all of those injections for (what felt like) eternity without her pumping me up with her motivational words and, most importantly, her amazing playlists of throwbacks! We jammed out to Missy Elliot (hands down best songs to shoot up to), Lizzo, Normani (also fabulous), Rihanna, N'SYNC, Backstreet Boys, Britney Spears, and more of those good old 90s hits.

We would FaceTime every night (she lived in Connecticut and I was in New Jersey) and she would get the jams going as I prepped my shots. This seriously got my mind off of what I had to do. I highly recommend doing this. I didn't feel the pain as much as I had in the past and I didn't feel as much pressure as I used to.

I'm not gonna lie: it still sucked. I never would've guessed that I'd be a pro at this, though.

Then it came time for the retrieval procedure. This required anesthesia, which meant I couldn't go by myself and I couldn't drive home from the appointment. It didn't occur to me that it would be a hospital-like experience until I got to the floor at RMA that does the retrievals and it took me right back to when I had my C-section (which was not the most beautiful experience).

I had to be hooked up to an IV, which I didn't expect. Even after being poked and prodded for months with blood work and injections, it still made me sick to my stomach to see yet another needle going into my skin. My husband couldn't look, of course. I don't think he realized what this procedure entailed either. Neither of us really did any extra research beyond what our doctors told us. We didn't want to worry or be freaked out.

Well, that didn't help me exactly, because I was still nervous as hell. I worried that they wouldn't get enough eggs, or something out of this world would go wrong. A couple days before, they had done a routine ultrasound and said there were not as many eggs as they had hoped for. That was all that sat on my mind for days. I didn't think this was going to work after all the hard work I had done for weeks leading up to this. My body only produced about 4–6 eggs while, on average, most women get about 13–18.

When it was time to go in, after all the doctors and nurses talked to me and got me prepped, I walked into the room and it was identical to the C-section table. It was a table shaped like a T, and they put my legs up, spread and in stirrups (strapped, might I add), and my arms were spread out. I was so nervous I was shaking from my head to my toes, so I guess it was a good thing I was strapped down.

I remember they were playing Aerosmith, "Sweet Emotion," which I've always enjoyed (even saw them in concert) and so I took that as a sign of good luck. They put the tubes around my face for the anesthesia and I was out within a minute or less. When I woke up, I was back in the recovery area and Jon was waiting for me. After I was able to hold down some juice and crackers, I was allowed to go home.

That was it. Thankfully, it wasn't nearly as painful as I thought it would be. It was more uncomfortable than anything. I rested for a couple days, even though my nurse said I didn't need to. I wanted to take the extra precautions for myself — for once.

The good news was that before we left RMA, they were able to tell us how many eggs they had retrieved, which was six. I was happy with that number, but also nervous because I knew that wouldn't necessarily equal six embryos. The way the retrieval works is, with the number of eggs taken out, that number (typically) goes down after it's fertilized with sperm. You hope that you get at least one good, fertilized embryo that makes it to the "blastocyst" stage. Well, we had to wait a week to find out how many (if any) made it to that golden status. It was agony because this was, in essence, the most important part. Without the embryos, you couldn't do a transfer, which couldn't lead to a baby.

Well, that day came. It was a Wednesday and I remember every little thing from when I got that call. Thankfully, I was on a prep block at work because I saw that number pop up on my phone and my stomach was instantly in knots. I picked up and my nurse said, "It's good news! Three embryos made it!"

I got chills all over my body and I had tears in my eyes. I couldn't believe it. After hearing this, I had that feeling that everything would be okay. I called my husband immediately and I could hear the joy and relief in his voice, just as I had felt with that call. It was a good day.

Then there was the last step of the IVF cycle: the transfer stage. This is (as it states) where the embryo is literally transferred to your uterus. This was the most exciting part! No anesthesia, nothing foreign, just some nice calming music and happy thoughts.

We went into the same procedure area as the retrieval, except this time it was a private room with nothing but a bed for me. The only trick was that I had to drink about 10oz or so of water right before my appointment so that I had a full bladder. This is so that, on the ultrasound, they can clearly see my uterus and where to place the embryo. That was probably the hardest part — having a full bladder and having to deal with a clamp and tube going into my vagina. Not cool.

I should probably back up and tell you the prep work for the transfer because it wasn't peaches and cream. It was definitely less than the others I've gone through, but still not easy. This time it was getting my body ready to support a pregnancy.

I started with Estradiol pills taken orally, which was a piece of cake compared to everything else. I had to take those twice a day, then it bumped up to three times a day. Meanwhile, every 3–4 days I had to go for blood work and an ultrasound to be monitored.

I remember my doctor bumping me back down to twice a day on the pill and then I began progesterone shots. Those were a bit different than the others. The needle was different. It was a longer syringe and a longer needle. It didn't come with an easy push button like the Follistim pen (one of the injections I used for most of the fertility treatments). The other catch was that it had to be injected in my lower back/buttocks region. Therefore, it was best to have someone else do it.

Well, people, when I tell you that my husband cannot handle needles, I really mean it. The last two times he had to get blood work or a flu shot, he actually fainted and I received a call from the nurses taking care of him. This was no joke.

Here is where my issue lay: the shots had to be done between 6 and 8 am each morning. If my husband couldn't do it, then who would? I didn't have family that was close by and could stop over each morning. I had to figure it out.

After some time, some talks, and some hugs my husband said he could do it. I must have asked him a hundred times, "Are you sure you can handle it? This is not easy." I knew I could call on one of my dear friends to help me if I was really stuck, but I also wanted my husband to be a part of this journey. I think it made a difference to have him actually do something physically to help me.

Well, I can tell ya, I was pleasantly surprised! He did so well with giving me those injections. I couldn't believe it. There were a couple of days that were more painful than others, more blood than the last time, but I was so proud of my hubby for handling that. That made two of us, who were afraid of needles, now fearless! It was quite an obstacle to overcome together. Now we're like pros!

I wish I could tell you all I needed was one round of IVF, but that's not my story, unfortunately.

As I wrote this section, I was in the middle of my second transfer. I didn't know what the outcome would be. I discussed with my therapist several times, whatever the "end" looked like is what it would be. I couldn't control it. We were doing everything in our power to help make a baby. As painful as it was to imagine my life without another one, I believed that there was a plan for us. I knew that maybe my path was meant to only have one child, and for that I was grateful. However, there would always be a part of me that would long for another baby.

"I put the test on the bathroom sink and just *scrolled* through Instagram until I was ready to look. After a few minutes I *decided to look* at the test and I couldn't believe it. *There was a line!* I yelled for Elicia and she came and she saw it too. I was excited and *hopeful* but I didn't want to get ahead of myself. The following day I took another

test and the line was even darker. I took a test *every day* until I went in for bloodwork at my *fertility clinic.* That day my doctor called me with the news that my HCG levels were amazing and that I was indeed *pregnant!* After *2.5 years* of waiting and hoping, it was the best feeling and we couldn't wait to be *moms."*
—Kelly

The Call

It was New Year's Eve, 2019. I went in that morning for blood work. It was the blood work that would tell me yes, or no. Our second transfer was done on December 23rd. We didn't tell a soul; not even our own parents. We decided that after our first transfer ended in a loss, we didn't want to go on that roller coaster again of telling our families and friends about all the details. It was a lot for us.

That morning, when I got back around 7 am or so, I stayed as busy as I could. My mind was racing (as it always was on those days). It was agony watching the clock, but I had an idea of the time we usually got the phone call. Usually, the nurse would call anywhere between 10:30 am and 1:30 pm. They were efficient with how they ran things there and everything was like clockwork.

To my surprise, it was only around 9 or 9:30 in the morning and I was in the family room about to sit on the couch when I saw the number on my Apple Watch. I immediately started to panic and screamed "JON! It's them!"

I ran to get my phone, answered, and put it on speaker for both of us to hear. This time it was not "No Caller ID," but it didn't trigger anything in my mind that it was good or bad — I just wanted to hear the news I'd been waiting for! It was a nurse — not my usual one because she was on vacation, so I couldn't tell from her tone of voice if it was happy or sad news — and she said, "Hello."

I forget whatever other small talk she made because the next thing I heard was, "*Congratulations! You have a positive pregnancy test!*"

I could not believe what she had just told me. I remember saying, "Are you serious?!" And then I fell to my knees and just started sobbing. I was crying so much I forgot that my nurse was still on the phone. I said, "I'm so sorry, but we've been waiting so long for this!"

Why did I even apologize? How else could I possibly have responded to such incredible, miraculous news? I'm sure she had heard this reaction many times before. So I was crying, my husband was crying, and then Tyler came running over.

"What's wrong mommy?"

I instantly hugged him and held him close, just breathing and thinking, "Thank you, God."

I got back on the phone with the nurse so that she could give me the levels of all my hormones and further directions. Unfortunately, I still had to continue with progesterone injections in my tush. I was fine with it now, but you know what? I was still nervous. I thought, "It took me two years to get pregnant. What if…? What if something goes wrong?"

I know of so many friends who have suffered pregnancy losses (I hate the word miscarriage — it sounds awful). This was in the back of my mind at every moment. I was worried. I was happy, so happy, but I almost didn't believe it could be true. With all the struggles and heartaches we'd had over the past two years, there we were with a positive pregnancy test.

I had to go back in for blood work two days after the test, "just to make sure the levels are continuing to rise" — yeah, because that didn't worry me even more. I thought to myself, "There it is, something could happen." Not that I'm always thinking negatively about this, but when you've failed month after month, you feel like it will never happen. Thankfully, all the blood work came back great and everything was rising nicely. The next step was blood work *and* an ultrasound a week later to check everything. I was so excited for that first ultrasound.

We are one of the lucky ones to have a happy ending to this difficult journey. I know that. I almost feel guilty about it. This is what I've been praying for, hoping for, and dreaming about for way too long and here I am.

"...I know that God has a *plan* for us, which is a *trust* that I don't think I would've ever had if I hadn't gone through this *struggle*."
—Vicki

The Journey's Over

Wrong!

I hoped and prayed every day, every month, every second that this time it would work, this time it was it. Then when it actually happened, I thought, "Holy shit. Is this real? This is actually happening." And then I went back to hoping and praying, except this time I was thinking, "Please God, please see this pregnancy to full-term. Please God, please let this baby be healthy and happy. Please God, let me have a healthy and smooth pregnancy."

The worrying does not stop, at least not for me. Don't get me wrong: I am so thankful and so happy that I am one of the lucky ones to have a happy ending. However, as each day passed, a part of me thought about the what-ifs. Each time I went in for routine blood work and ultrasounds, my heart skipped a couple beats as I wondered if my levels were rising, if they'd stopped, or worse, if they'd decreased. Every time I went in for an ultrasound, I'd breathe a sigh of relief when I heard that heartbeat. Every time I pulled into the parking lot of RMA and started walking up the path to the doors, my stomach would do flips. There was always the thought that something could go wrong because it took me so long to get to where we were.

I'd say I was kind of in a fog. In my mind, I knew I was pregnant. I felt all the symptoms, I saw each ultrasound. However, on a day-to-day basis I almost forgot. I think I had put up a wall like you do after a bad breakup; staying strong and putting up defenses so nothing bad can hurt you again. I kept breathing another sigh of relief as each week passed and we got closer to being out of the first trimester. I knew this didn't mean I was completely safe, but I also knew the risk for miscarriage drops dramatically after 12–14 weeks.

Yes, that was what I was afraid of. I was so afraid something would happen to my baby. I know it's so terrible to think that, but that's what happens after so many failures. It's hard to comprehend that what I wanted for so long has actually been given to me. I'd think, "What was different this time? Was it just the right time?"

Maybe. Who knows?

This pregnancy was not easy from the start. Shortly after we got the positive test results, I started to have spotting. I know it's very common for many women; however, it wasn't common for me. My first pregnancy with my son was almost flawless. I was very tired in the first and last trimester, but only had a two-week period of migraines. I was very fortunate to have such a wonderful pregnancy. I truly loved being pregnant and carrying my baby boy.

This time felt very different. I had constant spotting almost every day in the beginning. Later, I had two episodes of increased bleeding. The second one was the worst. It was lunchtime and I was at work, and all of a sudden I felt light headed and wanted to throw up. I went to the bathroom immediately and saw I was bleeding bright red as if I had my period.

I knew this was bad. I knew this was not normal. I quickly got my plans together for the afternoon, called the office to get coverage, picked up my son from preschool, and jetted out of there. I remember seeing my friend, Stacey, and just crying; telling her how scared I was. I was so worried that I was going to lose this baby right then and there.

I tried to stay positive and focused on getting to the doctors. Thankfully, my sister was staying with me so I was able to drop my son off and head straight to RMA. I was still bleeding. It was so much blood. All that was running through my mind was, "Please don't let this be a miscarriage." I was crying, feeling so anxious and I couldn't get there quick enough. Thankfully, RMA was only about 20 minutes from my house.

I pulled in and walked as fast as I could to the office, feeling like crap, bleeding worse than my normal period. I was scared shitless. I remember waiting in the room, and when my doctor came in I just started crying. He could see how scared I was. He was wonderful and comforted and reassured me that whatever it was, it would be. I breathed a bit easier and he got the ultrasound going. And there it was.

The baby was okay. *The baby was okay.* I was even able to hear the heartbeat, which made me cry again. How could this be? It truly was a miracle. I was so sure something terrible had happened. My doctor said it was a blood clot and that it could continue for days.

They had found a subchorionic bleed the first time I had a bleeding episode. A subchorionic bleed (also known as a sub-chorionic hematoma) is the accumulation of blood between the uterine lining and the chorion (the outer fetal membrane, next to the uterus) or under the placenta itself.[1] In other words, I had a blood clot in my uterus right next to the pregnancy sac, and it was the same size as the pregnancy sac. They didn't know what the exact reason was, it could've been the implantation or my placenta forming. The good news was that it should go away on its own by the end of the first trimester.

The bleeding did continue for at least a couple weeks. He told me that if it had gotten worse to the point where it was like hemorrhaging, then I would need to go to the ER. It was such an uneasy time for me. He recommended I take a few days off from work to rest and I couldn't do any physical activity until further notice. The bleeding needed to stop.

I was a mess. I had never experienced this before. Here I was, having intense things happen to me very early on in my pregnancy. I was so nervous something would go wrong after all we had been through. But I knew there was nothing I could do. My doctor told me specifically there was nothing he or I could do to change the future. Even though that was hard to hear, it was also reassuring. Deep down, I knew that the uncertainty of the future drove me crazy, though.

My doctor's orders were to rest and do no strenuous exercise. I took him seriously and rested for the next few days. I took time off from work and put my feet up. Along with the bleeding, I had cramping, like a period almost. It didn't feel good at all. At that point, I knew I needed to make myself a priority.

I took it one day at a time because that's all I could do. I remember during one of my ultrasounds at my regular OBGYN, around my 13-week checkup, the tech and I were talking and she obviously had my chart and knew that I got pregnant from IVF. I told her about how I was constantly worrying and just hoping everything would go well and that I'd have a healthy baby. This was after she saw the blood clot on the screen. She told me one of her babies was through IVF too, and you never really stop worrying until that baby is in your arms, safe and sound. I was hoping she wasn't right, but here I was, still thinking about everything that could happen — good and bad.

Why couldn't I just let go and be 100 percent happy? I'll tell you why. Because I've had too many bad things happen to me along the way. I've experienced too many emotional let downs. I've cried too much, mourned too much, grieved too much.

Each day, I try to think about how lucky I am. I try to really embrace it and soak it all in. I'm getting there, a little bit at a time. I heard some advice the other day that was something along the lines of, "You cannot push someone to just 'get over it.' They will heal in their own time."

This spoke to me in a way that made me feel understood. It made me feel that I wasn't crazy. Sometimes you think that way: "Am I depressed? Am I wrong for feeling this way?" I think if you make time for yourself each day, think about your emotions, and make a conscious effort to keep taking steps forward, you're going to be okay. If I told myself this a year or two ago, I probably wouldn't have believed it. But I think this goes to show that I have been healing in my own way; continuing to follow my path and do things for me.

Fast forward to 22 weeks and I was still on edge, I still wondered what my future would hold. I was feeling the baby kicks more and more, which was surreal. It was like I had forgotten what it felt like, but I never forgot how amazing the feeling was. Every kick put me at ease a little more. I'd stay still for as long as it took to feel another one, just so I knew I wasn't imagining it. In those moments, I knew everything would be okay.

"It was honestly the most *wonderful* way to tell us, and I can remember *that moment* pretty vividly actually. Sitting in Dad's kitchen and just *hanging out,* trying to distract us all from everything going on with Dad and all the *complications* surrounding that. When you told

us, I just felt *overwhelming joy* and heartbreak. I was so happy it had finally *worked,* that Dad got to hear that he was going to be a *grandpa again.* And it immediately hit that he probably wouldn't ever get to *meet them,* so of course I broke down."
—Sonia

Life After the Good News

That New Year's Eve day, we cried and could hardly believe that our dream had finally come true. We had hoped and prayed for this for years and we finally got our rainbow baby. Christmas had just happened, and that was my absolute favorite holiday. I was in the best of spirits. It was New Years Eve, the start of a new year; a fresh start. All the stars were aligning. Everything was so, so good ... or so I thought.

It came time to go to my ultrasound and check that the yolk was there, which is the first sign of pregnancy on the ultrasound monitor. During the scan, though, they couldn't find it. I was so happy walking into that room, but literally all of that joy turned into panic immediately.

It was quiet in the room, with two nurses and two doctors. They had the second doctor come in to do another scan and double check what the first doctor couldn't find. It was what they had suspected: nothing on the monitor.

I started to worry. The doctors said it was still a bit early (I was around 5 weeks pregnant at this point) so they wanted me to come back in a few days to do another ultrasound and blood work. The only thing that was keeping me hopeful was that my blood work came back with great results, showing that my levels were rising. I was still freaking out, though. Not to mention that, during that week, my doctor had told me, "Stay positive but also be prepared."

That's all I could think until the next appointment. All sorts of things were running through my head, and of course, one of them was miscarriage. My doctor said "be prepared" for that very reason. I was a nervous wreck, but tried to stay occupied and keep my mind from thinking the worst.

When the day finally came to get another ultrasound, I was so anxious and nervous I couldn't wait to get that scan done. It was a miracle — the doctor found it on the first try! They said they thought they saw something last time, though they couldn't be sure, but this confirmed it was the yolk.

Thank you, God! I breathed a sigh of relief and immediately called my husband as I was walking out of the clinic. I thought, "Okay, I think it'll be okay."

But from the beginning of this journey, all I had ever done was stay positive and, also, prepared myself for the worst. I had done exactly that every single month, only to be let down, so was I feeling 100 percent strong about this? No, I always had my doubts. I guess you could say I was trying to guard my heart from experiencing another painful letdown. I couldn't let myself let go of that wall just yet.

Then, January came around and everything came crashing to a halt. I got the worst news after going back to school from winter break.

I'll back up a bit and give you a little insight into what had been going on before the holidays, before my transfers, before we had any good news. My dad had gotten sick in the middle of November. He started having severe pains in his stomach. It didn't go away so he went to the hospital. They diagnosed him with pancreatitis. After a week, he was sent home. He changed his diet, as you should if you have pancreatitis, and he was supposed to feel better shortly after doing so.

He didn't. His pain started to increase. He went to different doctors and was in and out of the hospital until he finally went to Yale Smilow Cancer Center for further testing. With Thanksgiving, Christmas, and New Years, his testing and visits got delayed. It wasn't until the first week of January, after I had returned to work and a week after our great news, that we learned he was diagnosed with Pancreatic Cancer.

I remember my stepmom calling me. I couldn't get ahold of my dad. He wasn't returning my calls or texts and I had been checking in with him every single day since he had started having these pains. He would answer me quickly or at most within a couple of hours. I was worried and afraid. Deep down, I had known it was something serious since the beginning. To actually hear what I had been thinking all along was devastating.

I sobbed and sobbed over the phone. I couldn't believe it. This wasn't fair. My dad was going to be a grandpa again. People would tell me there was hope and there have been so many advancements in pancreatic cancer treatments, but I didn't believe it. I knew this was bad. Really bad. Everyone knows how serious pancreatic cancer is. Everyone knows it's only a matter of time, but you never know exactly how much.

After hearing the news and talking with my stepmom, my siblings, and eventually my dad the next day, we swallowed it and tried to mentally prepare ourselves for what was ahead.

How bad was it? When would chemo start? What would happen to our dad while he went through all of this?

Millions of questions and worries went through my head. I was, and still am, a complete worrier. I think about all the what-ifs, which ultimately stresses me out. I've come to realize that, as I've gotten older, and especially after becoming a mother, I worry more than when I was younger. This, of course, does not help when you are newly pregnant and really need to be careful.

I tried to breathe and stay as calm as possible. I got the news on a Monday and immediately drove to Connecticut to be with my dad that weekend. We had seen each other at Christmas and we all saw that he had dropped weight. When I saw him almost two weeks later, we noticed even more weight loss.

No one wanted to say it. My dad was still in great spirits. He put on a happy face and was trying his best to be his old joking self. But I could see it. I could see the pain he had, especially when he laughed. He would hold his stomach or his side and cringe a little. He didn't want us to see him in pain.

While I visited that weekend, he had multiple calls from different doctors, pain management, oncologist, nurses; you name it. Never mind the medications he had to take and the cost of all of it. It was in the middle of talking about all of this in my dad's kitchen — me, my sister, my stepmom and my dad — that I just thought, "I'm going to give them some positive things to think about."

As I said, my whole family knew what my husband and I had been going through and what a tough road it had been. Jonathan and I had talked about sharing the news with my dad before I went up to see him. So, in the middle of the conversation in the kitchen, I just said, "Well, I think it's a good time for some good news," as I looked at all of them. They stared back at me with looks that said, "Could this be it?"

And I told them, "I'm pregnant!!"

We all broke out into screaming, crying and cheering. I hugged my dad so tight. My sister was sobbing her eyes out (she was with me through every single step of the way). My stepmom was so happy. We all hugged and cheered and cried. It was a really great, happy moment. And then I said something along the lines of, "Now we gotta beat this cancer for the baby."

I wish I could say it was uphill from there and I had a happy ending in this. Originally, we thought he was stage 3 and then further testing and blood work weeks later showed it had metastasized and was stage 4. He wasn't eating still and he continued to be in pain no matter what medications he took. He was on some strong stuff.

I made sure that my husband and son made a trip up to spend time with him one last time. At least, in my head that's what I thought, but I never imagined it really would be. While all of this was going on, I almost forgot that I was pregnant. There were so many other emotions that took over me and my mind. It was early. I wasn't showing so it could be out of sight, out of mind.

I worried about my dad. I worried about losing him. However, other worries came into play which I never told my dad about. The day after I told him I was pregnant, which was around 6 weeks, I started to have spotting, which then turned into bleeding. I remember leaving Connecticut earlier so that I could go to RMA the next day and check everything. This was when they found the subchorionic bleed.

While this bleeding continued, my dad got worse. This was all happening around mid- to late-January of 2020. By the end of January, he was admitted to the hospital and, little did we know, he wouldn't come back home. I continued to travel every weekend to Connecticut to spend time with him and help with whatever I could. I swear there was something every week while he was there — an infection here, a procedure there — just so, so much. He continued to lose weight and it killed us to see him like that.

On February 20th, I decided to bring my son up for a trip. I remember every single day from this moment on, and I relive it often. It was a Thursday and I took time off from work and took Tyler out of school. Previously, I had been making arrangements for him to be brought to and from school (I would take off a Friday or Monday to extend the weekends). So this time, I decided to make it easy on everyone and bring Tyler with me and have my mom spend some time with him.

That Thursday, we arrived early in the day. Once I dropped off my son at my mom's, I headed to the hospital. My brother, sister and I kind of all took turns staying at the hospital. My sister was spending nights there and sometimes my brother as well. I would stay during the day while I was there each weekend. This day, though, was different. My dad was in good spirits. He even ate a little bit and walked in the hallway! This hadn't happened in a while. I was so proud of him. I remember thinking that he was turning a corner.

Friday morning, February 21st, everything changed. My step-mother had called me and told me to get to the hospital as soon as possible. Something had happened and it could be the end. I remember being absolutely shocked. I was running through my mind how great yesterday had been; to be with him, talk to him, see him walk with a walker down the hallway. Now this?

I couldn't even put two feet in front of me. I was in the car about to leave for the hospital when I got the phone call. I knew my sister was in the shower and I wasn't sure if I should go back in or get to the hospital. We eventually rushed out the door and got there together.

We walked in the room and everything was different. He

wasn't even conscious. He couldn't speak. There were doctors and nurses around. Even though I had thought about this happening deep in the back of my mind, when it was staring me in the face it was devastating. I fell to my knees at his bedside and just cried in his hands saying, "No, dad, no!" I thought, "This is too fast, this can't be happening." But it was.

That day and that weekend, so many friends came. Close friends, family friends we knew since I was a kid, coworkers — you name it. It was so difficult to see these people and think of all the good times we had together and now this. It wasn't fair. My baby bump was just starting to show. My dad was going to be "Pop Pop" round two. He was never going to meet this miracle babe.

I remember every single moment of those last few days. That Sunday, we each took turns having time alone with him to talk to him and tell him whatever was on our minds. He couldn't respond back, really, but there were moments when he would blink or make some sort of motion or noise in response. I remember his breathing. It was heavy and congested. It got worse over the weekend. It got bad. Eventually he had secretions coming out of his mouth.

This was such an incredibly difficult time for me. Not only was I off to a rough start with this pregnancy, but I had all this going on too. I was in a hospital every week (before the COVID-19 lockdown) and trying to make sure I was taking care of myself as much as I could. I had talked to the nurses and told them I was pregnant and asked them what precautions I should take from the beginning. I had been wearing masks on that floor and in my dad's room for a while, just to be safe. Then, I started wearing gloves too.

Once my dad took a turn for the worse, they found that his

secretions had bacteria and we all had to mask up and wear gloves and gowns. This was all so upsetting. We hated to see him like this. It was so painful. We thought that maybe we all needed to give him peace and space to go peacefully. My brother, sister, and I went down to the cafeteria Sunday night to let him have his time. We were gone for about an hour. We came back up and he was still there for us.

The next day, Monday, February 24th, was the day he passed. That morning, hospice had told us that he looked different and this would probably be the day. I remember the exact moment. It was 4:45 pm. My sister and I were on either side of his bed. My brother went to get some water from the refreshment room. We put on some Tom Cruise movie to kind of get our minds off of everything. All of a sudden, it was very quiet. My sister called my name. We looked over and he had stopped breathing. We knew it because his breathing for the past few days had been heavy and congested. I ran to get my brother down the hall and tell a nurse to come quick, only to come back to find him taking his very last breaths. That was it.

The three of us stayed until they came to take him to the morgue a couple hours later. We gathered up all of his belongings, crying as we did. They came to take him away a couple of hours later and I will never, ever forget my last moments with my father, as they wheeled him down the hallway. I remember just clutching my belly while tears rolled down my face.

The next week was a blur, but also felt like eternity. Planning funeral arrangements, the obituary, the card that everyone gets at the funeral — there's a lot of work to do after someone dies. You're a wreck from just losing your father, but then you have to plan and prep so many things for someone's funeral. We had to choose and print photos for display boards and frames, we had to pick out urns that we wanted (he wanted to be cremated, which at first shocked me but then comforted me because we all got a part of him), we had to prepare speeches for the eulogy — the list went on. It was a lot, but I think it also brought us some comfort and helped us mourn.

Going through these motions while pregnant was even harder. Thinking about the future without my dad, or Pop Pop as my son called him, was real hard. Those last moments I had with him alone, I told him, "Please watch over us. Let this baby be healthy and happy and give me a sign that you're okay."

We got through that week. We got through that funeral. We got back to "normal life" after that. And then COVID-19 hit two weeks later.

"Who would have *thought* that we would continue to be tested, even after going through so many *trials and tribulations?* Now we would face a global pandemic, in isolation, while *pregnant* and working from home."
—Me

Coronavirus and Pregnancy

We all know what a mess COVID-19 has been. Add in being pregnant and everything goes up a notch. This was just the continuation of my shit show of a year. I was literally getting back to work after my dad's passing, trying to adjust to "normal" life of working and the whole nine yards.

I was back at work a week before the commotion about the virus got serious. I remember it exactly, Monday, March 2nd. I was back in Jersey and had a prenatal doctor's appointment and then I went to work on Tuesday, March 3rd, for the first time in a couple weeks. It was weird and surreal, but it was great to see the kids' faces and get hugs from them. They knew what had happened because I felt it was necessary for me to inform their parents of why I had been gone for so long.

I've always found being honest and upfront, especially with the people you work with, to be extremely helpful. It creates meaningful relationships. I think I got that from both my mom and dad. My mom is huge on honesty, kindness, and friendship (and has a ton of friends because of this), but also my dad was such a warm and happy guy. He would always say hello to anyone he saw in a coffee shop, store, or wherever he was. He always had a smile on his face, too. So many people would tell me, as they shook my hand and gave their condolences at his funeral, "You have your dad's smile."

That made me smile, but also tore me up inside.

Going back to work was good for me. It was especially nice to get back into a routine, which was also really good for Tyler (since he attends Pre-K at my school). That first week back felt great. I was also in a daze, really, trying to process what I had just been through.

I couldn't believe my dad was no longer there. It was weird. I would teach and have flashbacks of conversations we had or moments we shared about teaching. In my very first classroom, he had come to check it out and help me. He had brought his dog, Riley. I remember the exact picture we took, standing in front of my very first teacher desk (Man, was I skinny back then!).

The mind is such an incredible thing. Why would it bring these memories to me? Obviously, I was back to doing what I loved and I remember my dad was so proud of me getting my first job as a teacher. I remember before I decided to be a teacher, I was in the marketing industry working in Manhattan for an advertising agency. It was so much fun and I met incredible people, but it also paid terribly and I wasn't fully satisfied with the work I was doing. It wasn't for me, but I was grateful for that experience and the connections I made. I believe you can learn from every opportunity and it can shape who you are, if you let it.

I flashed back to all of these memories and thoughts in the middle of my day, while teaching. That's what I meant when it was like I was in a fog that week. Of course, I knew it would take some adjusting. Everyone sharing their condolences or giving me a smile of pity or sorrow was difficult, but not as hard as I thought it would be.

Then the news started hitting at the end of that week and over the weekend; about the virus that was first observed in Wuhan, China.[1] I remember watching the news footage about that wildlife market, and I wanted to throw up. Seeing that it could travel to the United States, I thought about all the crazy movies about diseases that would spread. (Even World War Z! Yeah, I know, I got ahead of myself.)

The following week everyone was talking about what could happen and speculating about schools possibly being closed. We had a meeting mid-week and our boss told us that if we close it could be for up to three weeks and that we would have to prepare lesson plans for distance learning so we wouldn't have to make it up. I remember thinking it would be great to work from home for a few weeks. Then, Thursday came along and there was word that some schools in Pennsylvania were closed because someone came in contact with a person who had the virus.

That night, I remember starting to draft lesson plans, just in case. In addition to all this commotion, my son had been pretty sick with (what I thought was) the stomach bug. It started one night with him throwing up twice, then feeling weak with no ap- petite the next day. I figured it was a stomach bug and he would be good by Tuesday. However, life just wasn't going to be easy for me so there I was, calling in so that I could be home with Tyler because he was still weak and couldn't eat. This was all happen- ing less than a week after getting back from my dad's funeral.

My son ended up being out sick that whole week. It took me, my husband, my mother-in-law, and my mom to travel from Connecticut to come and watch him while we went to work. It was already bad enough that I had taken another day off after being out of work for almost two weeks and then anticipating being out of school for weeks. I needed to be at work.

It actually was nice that my mom was able to come at the end of the week to be with my son because that was the last time we got to see her for months. We didn't think it would be that long, but knew it could be for a period of time. I was used to going to Connecticut at least once a month. It was only a two hour drive and Tyler did great in the car, since we had always done that. I didn't realize how much I'd miss seeing and being with my family until all of this COVID stuff got serious.

No one knew how bad it was until we were living it. We thought it would only be a few weeks of being at home, which then turned into months, which turned me into a crazy person (like I wasn't already!).

It was nice in the beginning, not having to make lunches or rush out the door each morning. I made a schedule for the morning for Tyler so that we had structure and routine. I was ready to do this! This was like my dream, to be able to have coffee and check my emails in the morning calmly and in my own kitchen, while having *The Today Show* on. It was magical!

Of course, having my husband home was different too because he was working (also in education) and we were both busy, in the mornings especially.

We got into the groove of the new "routine"; getting dressed for the day (by which I mean changing from pajamas to leggings), coming downstairs to make coffee, and turning the TV on for Tyler. Everyone would settle into the day and it was calm, for the most part. Then, as the weeks went on, the academics had to be ramped up. The expectations were raised. Everything was more, more, more.

At first, I was able to balance working and teaching my son, and I felt good about it. Once schools continued to be closed and the work we had sent home wasn't enough, we had to transition to Google Classroom and teach new lessons, grade assignments online, answer emails (as we did before), create teaching videos, hold Google Meets — the list goes on. That was all fine and I understood why we were doing it, but it took away from my time with Tyler. It became very difficult to do our jobs while making sure he was engaged and taken care of.

My husband's work got more demanding as well. He also taught college courses online at night via Zoom or Google Meet. It was all very different than what I had imagined "working from home" was actually like. I thought I would love it; I thought I could handle it. I kept telling myself that this was not the norm, which is why it felt so isolating and confined. I thought I wanted to be a stay-at-home mom, but after experiencing this, I didn't know if that's what I wanted anymore.

Now, I know this is not truly what both of those jobs are like. We were in a pandemic, a lockdown. We were not allowed to go anywhere besides the grocery store, or see anyone besides the people we lived with in our households. What the hell kind of life is that?

I'm a home-body, an introvert for the most part, and it was affecting me more than I ever expected it would. My husband, on the other hand, is an extrovert, big time. He never sits still and is always working on something.

He was pretty calm in the beginning — which surprised me. He did great overall, but once lockdown lasted for close to two months he started to get agitated. Of course, I can't blame him. We are human. Socializing is the main part of our lives and it was stripped away from us. I tried to remind him of the positives: FaceTime, Google Meets, phone calls, outdoor visits. We did all of those, including outdoor visits with his family, some friends of ours, and my mom and sister. It felt good to be around them, but also awkward. It's family and friends that you love and you want to think, "It's okay, it's them, they can't have it," but you just don't know. It was especially hard to distance from the grandparents.

Like I said, I was pregnant, so bring on the hormones, the worry, the panic. We had the outdoor visits, which I was fine with. No one came in the house for anything.

Then, my mom and sister surprised me on Mother's Day all the way from Connecticut! I was so happy, I was crying. My sister called me and said, "Gosh it's so hot outside, isn't it?"

I knew right away she was messing with me, and I just said, "Shut up, what are you doing?"

I ran downstairs and saw their car through the window and just started screaming, "NO!" And then I lost it. I was so happy and sad all at the same time. I didn't realize how much I had missed them until then. I was halfway through my pregnancy and the only real times my family had seen me was through misery; throughout the months of my father's illness and death. My dad was diagnosed the first week of January, 2020 and I didn't start telling my immediate family about my pregnancy until mid-February. Then, my father passed on February 24th. At the beginning of March, we all went into lockdown.

While pregnant, I had to be extra cautious. They didn't know all the side effects of what could happen with the pregnancy or the baby, but there had been some cases. I heard of moms who had the virus going into labor early, and complications with them and their babies. There have also been success stories, but those mothers and babies went through hell to get better.

I was supposed to have my Fetal Echo Heart Exam in April, 2020, but they had to cancel the appointment due to the virus. The doctor asked me a bunch of health screening questions and said that with that, and looking over my chart, since I was a low risk patient they didn't want me coming in with the high chance that I could get the virus.

She basically said that it wasn't worth going in when the baby had a low risk of having any heart conditions. Of course, she couldn't guarantee that, but said it wasn't worth me getting the virus due to the fact that it could cause complications in my pregnancy and other repercussions that they didn't have research for yet.

That was all she had to say for me to understand how serious this could be for me. This, of course, caused more anxiety. This year just continued to be full of worry, anxiety, and fear.

I feel like my pregnancy joy was tainted; like I wasn't able to fully enjoy this miracle in our lives. I know it's probably terrible to say, but that's how I feel. It was one thing after the next of bad news ever since we found out we were pregnant. I'd send pictures to my family randomly of my growing belly, trying to enjoy it. I didn't do it as much as I had with my son, and I don't know why. I got somewhat past the point of feeling — I don't even know what the feeling was — the fear of something going wrong?

No, I take that back. I always worried about that in the back of my mind because you truly never know. Anything could happen.

I guess what I mean to say is that I was finally ready to embrace this pregnancy and enjoy it, but I couldn't do it the way I had dreamed of. I wanted to have a great summer of seeing family and friends; of basking in the glory of this big belly that I had dreamed of for so long! I wanted to have a party, or sprinkle, or whatever they call it. Yes, I'm going to be selfish and say that I wanted that. Before any of this happened to me, I would've told you sprinkles are just a way of getting money and things out of people — "You already had a baby shower. Why are you doing it again?"

But now, that's not what I see. I see it as a celebration of yet another miracle. I didn't want the presents or the money or all the extra; I simply wanted to spend time with my family and friends and have a party outside. That's it. I just wanted to fully enjoy this baby girl on the way and take it all in. I feel like COVID robbed me of that. It took me away from my family, my friends, and (most of the time) my joy.

As I was scrolling on Instagram, I found an artist who painted a picture of an embryo. It was beautiful and all I could think of was painting one myself. I couldn't stop thinking what a wonderful idea that was. I immediately got started with the painting. Once I finished, I just stared at it. I added the quote, "No great love ever came without great struggle. Life is tough my darling, but so are you," (Mahmood Buriro & Stephanie Bennett-Henry) next to it.

Then I just started crying; crying because I was in disbelief still that my miracle was happening; crying because I couldn't fully embrace the joy of this pregnancy when I was too scared of catching this goddamn virus; crying because I was still so nervous something could go wrong; crying because this quarantine absolutely sucked and made everything in creation stressful; crying because my dad wouldn't be around to see my baby born; crying because I felt invisible when all I wanted was to celebrate this baby girl.

All I wanted to do was fast forward and have my baby, safe and sound. I was nervous about the virus coming back in the fall. I didn't know what this delivery was going to be like during the pandemic. Would my husband be allowed in with me? God, I hoped so. Would my family be allowed to visit? Probably not. I was already making mental preparations in my head for my mom to quarantine herself before she came. I needed my mom with me. She had helped me so much when Tyler was born that I felt comfortable with being on my own after she left. There's something about a girl just needing her mom.

This pandemic created so many negative situations. It robbed people of special celebrations — weddings, bridal showers, bachelorette and bachelor parties, birthdays, graduations, baby showers … the list goes on.

I know I'm being negative, but I'm going to go there for a minute because it's only human. You can only be positive for so long. I know it's totally out of our own control and everyone is doing the best they can to figure this thing out and get a vaccine or therapy or whatever. That doesn't mean we can't be sad about the things we are missing out on.

It absolutely sucks. I want to hug my family. I want to be able to drive by their houses and hang outside for a little. I can't do any of those things because of this pandemic. Sure, could I take a day to drive up to my mom's? I could, but then what about bathroom stops? What about when I'm hungry? What about if it's really hot outside? What if someone is in the house at the same time as me or my son or my husband? All of these possibilities posed risks. We didn't know enough at the time about this virus and that made me nuts and extremely anxious. I just counted down the days until this baby's arrival. (This was all within the heat of the pandemic, March 13th, 2020, and continued through the birth of my daughter on September 2nd, 2020.)

As things began to open up in mid-June, more and more people were outside trying out a new "normal." For example, I was downtown where there's a beautiful waterfall, quaint shops and all, and it was packed on this gorgeous day. Yes, most people had masks on and everything was take-out or order from the window, but it felt really good to be outdoors and see people "out and about" like things were normal.

Mixed emotions run through my mind about it. I wanted to not have to worry about this, but I also couldn't let my guard down. I heard about those states that opened back up so quickly and had mass gatherings with barely any restrictions. Their cases increased drastically. It all made me very nervous. Another part of me wanted to fast forward to after having my baby, to have a little less worry. But would I worry less? Who the hell knew? It all depended on what happened over the next few months and what my doctors had to say.

Tuesday, June 16th, I went to my doctor's office for my 28-week checkup. I was so excited to see my baby girl on the ultrasound screen, especially since it had been two months since my last ultrasound. I was a bit nervous, too. I was worried that something could be wrong or off-schedule with her measurements. I was also having my glucose test done to check for gestational diabetes and such.

The checkup started off with someone new doing my ultrasound, which was fine. I didn't care. However, it was just so quick and I only got one picture! Normally, I saw these two women and we would chat for a while, and they would send me so many pictures and videos to share with family. I was a little bummed when I only got one. However, this was a big ultrasound, to check the baby's bladder, stomach, head, spine, etc.

I also asked them to double-check the amniotic fluid. That was the big one for me. Of course, it turned out I had excess of it again. It's called Polyhydramnios, where there is more than average amniotic fluid in the womb. This required me to be monitored more often with my son and now I would be doing the same with my daughter. It was an additional worry, one that I had been really trying to avoid.

I made sure to keep a healthy diet throughout my pregnancy and started exercising the moment I got the okay from my doctor (around the beginning of my second trimester). I stuck with a healthy diet throughout my first, second and third trimesters. The ultrasound tech said it can just happen, which was the same response as another doctor's. It could also mean a big baby or gestational diabetes. Keep the punches coming, I guess!

At another appointment, I had to get blood drawn an hour after I drank a bottle of liquid sugar. It didn't taste that bad — kind of like Sprite except thicker. Man, did it cause such heartburn shortly after. Anyway, you'd think getting blood drawn would be a piece of cake after all the blood work I had done throughout my fertility treatments, but no.

I've only had to get blood work done once or twice during my pregnancy, but those isolated times triggered something inside of me. It just reminded me of everything I had gone through. I thought back to the 5 am wake up calls; getting to RMA by 6 am and getting my blood drawn in a matter of minutes; all the prep I had to do in order to get that done before getting to work. Since my left arm was the one that usually worked, it got poked and prodded a lot. That adds up. Some weeks, I would get blood work done every couple days. I had gotten used to it, but over time scar tissue had built up. When that happens, it's more painful and more difficult to draw blood from that spot.

I started to dread blood work and hoped it wouldn't hurt. I remember one time, they couldn't get it on the first draw so they had to poke me again in another spot. It was the worst, but I sucked it up. That was just the first step. The next was receiving the results — whatever it was, good or bad.

Blood work meant a lot of things. For me, it was a hormone level check, a pregnancy test, a check if I could begin the next cycle or not, and it also checked my HCG levels after I was pregnant to make sure they kept rising (if they didn't that meant a nonviable pregnancy or possible miscarriage). It was so many more things than just getting blood, and it became more nerve-wracking than you could imagine.

I remember sitting in one of the many seats, waiting for the phlebotomist to come over and double check my name and social security number (which they did every single time). I just sat there thinking, "This test is a big one." Sometimes I would think they didn't draw enough blood or they did it wrong when my results would come back negative or bad, but I knew that was crazy talk.

This blood work for my 28-week checkup brought back a wave of thoughts, experiences, and emotions. Even five days after having the blood drawn I still had a bruise. The bruises I would get during my treatments were, to say the least, something. I know I'm lucky to look at my bruise on my arm right now and know that it's a good thing. It's during my pregnancy, no longer during treatments. I'm grateful for that, I really am. I just can't forget all that I've been through, and I don't think I should. It's a reminder of my strength and courage. It's a reminder of the struggle, the pain, and the obstacles I overcame to get where I am today.

I think about how I could have still been going through those treatments during the pandemic because that could've been quite possible. It could've also been possible to have been done with IVF and moved on to whatever lay ahead for me and my husband. I had discussed this with my therapist several times. I had finally gotten to the point of preparing myself mentally that I may have been destined for only one child. Even though there are all these treatments and medications and science behind infertility, it's never a guarantee of making a baby. That was a hard pill to swallow for a while, especially with how much was involved in this process.

I thank God that this is our plan. I thank my lucky stars, my guardian angels — every single thing. I truly was in shock when we got that positive news on New Years Eve because, honestly, part of me thought it just wouldn't work.

During the pandemic, I saw so many women on Instagram posting about their treatments being delayed or having to have multiple COVID tests done prior to starting their next cycles. That is a lot! It's already mentally draining to do the regular testing and appointments with your day-to-day life, but then add the safety measures for COVID — the stress levels go through the roof! And I know I've mentioned that stress does not help these matters. It only makes things worse.

These are seriously difficult times, but I truly believe everything happens for a reason. I know some people think that's a crock of shit, but I think there's a plan for every single one of us. We may not like that plan or understand what the reasoning behind an event is, but it's there for a purpose. Maybe later in life, we come to realize why something happened to us. It takes time, it takes energy, it takes working towards the future with positive intent. It takes a village.

As I reread this chapter, I thought back over the past nine months.

Nine months.

I never thought I would categorize those two words into the actual value of what it meant: pregnancy. I sat there a week away from the scheduled C-section that would bring this baby girl into my arms, and I'll tell you right now, I still didn't believe it. I could feel those strong kicks, like she had all the room in the world, but it was still surreal.

I think back to one of the first ultrasounds where the tech said to me, "You'll feel that way until you're holding your baby."

I thought then, "I hope it's not like this during the whole pregnancy," and yet there I was, still so anxious and counting down every second until this baby was here, safe and sound.

She was right, though. I would feel so much better when I held my baby in my arms. The whole time, I'd worried about her health, her growth, her progress. I'd thought about if I got sick with COVID, about what would happen to me — and worse — to her.

With the pandemic, it's mandatory to have a COVID-19 test done a week before your procedure. I went to the hospital to get it done, already grossed out by being there and thinking about the germs that are literally everywhere.

But the precautions are in place. I had to see the front desk, give my name, tell them what I was there for. They gave me a sticker with the date and such to put on my shirt. There were entire areas closed off, only three people were allowed in the elevator at a time, hand sanitizer stations were everywhere, obviously face masks were mandatory at all times, and more.

I got to the second floor for the testing, right next to the radiology department. It looked familiar, but it didn't click as to why at first. I turned right to go to the testing room and thought, "Here we go." I was ready for it to be unpleasant, but it turned out to be totally okay! It was the one where the swab goes up your nose, but I was able to do it myself! Stick the swab up one nostril, and go in circles 5–6 times, then do the next nostril, and finally stick it in the tube. It may have taken a total of one minute, thank God!

Walking out, I passed the radiology waiting room again and kept thinking, "Why is this familiar?" My mind flashed back to my dad in the hospital. Nope, wasn't the same hospital. And then it hit me. I came here right at the beginning of fertility testing, before I went to RMA, to get my hysterosalpingogram (HSG) testing done — the one where they flush fluids through the fallopian tubes to make sure there are no blockages.

Oh yeah, those were good times. Everything flashed before my eyes. I remembered having to lie on a table under one of those special radiology mats as they flushed fluids through my tubes and we all watched on the monitor as it went through. My husband was there with me, along with a nurse and my doctor.

Everything came full circle. I was on that same floor, nine months pregnant and thinking back to being there at the beginning of it all, almost two years before. I also had the same doctor that did my HSG perform my C-section for our second little babe.

It just makes you think: there has got to be a plan for each and every one of us.

"*Infertility* can definitely put a strain on your *marriage.* It makes it harder at times for sure, but what doesn't kill you *makes you stronger.* This was a very hard obstacle for us, but we got through it *together* — somehow."
—Me

An Interview with My Husband

When I planned to write this chapter, I pictured writing it the same as all the other chapters. However, Jon wanted me to simply have a conversation with him. I typed up a bunch of questions that came to mind and we just talked. I thought of things that I had been curious about throughout it all and maybe questions that were uncomfortable to answer during our process.

Of course, we communicated with each other as we were going through it, but now being on the other side, it was a little less stressful. I wondered what he would say. We talked while our son was napping one day and it turned out to be comforting, and at times eye-opening as I found he thought the same things as I did. Even though we talked about our feelings as we were moving through each step, it was still difficult. I don't think we opened up as much as we could have because it was so painful during the process. We were both suffering, so I don't think we wanted to push each other more than we already were. It was just a matter of "getting through it" at times. However, I believe the struggles you go through make you stronger. As I always knew, my husband is my rock — especially during the hard times.

I hope this conversation brings you some comfort, and maybe even allows you to open up to your partner to discuss things that may be really hard right now on your journey. Or maybe you're not ready to talk and you're in defense mode. I get that.

I was there too, and that's okay. Take your time and go at your own pace. That's all you can do. But when you're ready, maybe ask your partner some of these questions. You may find they are thinking and feeling the same way you are in a time that can be so lonely.

Q & A

What was your biggest fear?
All the time, effort, emotions and finances and no 100 percent guarantee. If you start this process, there should be something on the other end, but it doesn't always work that way. To decide to have a second kid and then not get it — after investing so much into it — that's hard.

Did you have hope each month, even after we were over a year in? Did it ever fade?
Yeah, I did every month because after your period it was like, "Oh, another chance." The worst was when we were a couple days late and I would always ask you, "What do you think? Is this the one?"

Did the hope ever fade?
Not really. It didn't fade because we had the resources — finances, health insurance, good doctors. There was always a next step. However, for IVF, after the first round failed, that was the hardest because there was no next step.

Did you have doubts?
No... (*He's stronger than me — I definitely had doubts.*)

What was it like to listen to/watch me do my shots in the beginning?
I would do my best to check out because I don't do well with needles, so it was great to have your sister be that person. However, once I started giving you the shots I started to feel more a part of the process and more connected to it.

What was it like to give me the shots for the first time?
It was easier in the morning because we had to go to work, and it was a routine that had to be done. It was a lot easier once I started doing it over and over.

What was it like to watch me month after month, especially after I lost hope and got more upset as time passed?
That was really difficult because you can't do anything. That's the hardest part of the whole process. I like to have control of my circumstances, but in this you have absolutely zero control. There was nothing I could do. Like saying sorry and giving a hug was ... ya know? Not enough.

When you went to RMA for your own visits, what did it feel like? What was going through your mind?
It was fine. I mean, it's awkward, but it wasn't horrible. You were in and out in minutes. It felt like a business transaction. It's weird and awkward.

Seeing all the different walks of life, it sometimes gave me more confidence because we were in our early 30s while I saw people who looked like they were in their late 40s. It made me think that maybe this would work for us. It was all demographics, too. There were young and old people, white, black, Asian, Indian — all ages, all races, all ethnicities — it didn't matter. It wasn't just one type of person. Also, it made me feel that we are

not alone. This was a huge place — this is no isolated incident …
this was/is big.

Did you ever think it would never work?
Probably after the first IVF round failing because that's the top
of the food chain. And because it was approaching the holidays
and I thought, "If God's not going to give it to us at this time…
then will he at all?"

What was the hardest part of this journey for you?
Just understanding. I kept going back to how no one found any
issues. We were both healthy individuals, in the okay age range,
and we didn't have issues the first time. So everything in my
mind said we should be popping kids out, no big deal. The first
doctor said, "Oh, it's your sperm morphology." Then another
doctor said it was high and it wasn't an issue. Plus, seeing other
people who are older and not living healthy lifestyles get pregnant was extremely difficult. Trying to be happy for those people
is also hard because you want to be happy for them and you are,
but you're also sad for yourself and us. You know there's other
people, but social media makes you feel alone because it damn
sure feels like you're alone when you see all the pregnancy posts
and news.

What kept you going and helped you stay positive?
That we had resources, there was a next step, and that there was
nothing wrong with us. It was just not the right sperm with the
right egg — or at least from what we concluded, there was nothing wrong with us.

Anything that came to mind that you never told me?

That it was somewhat my fault. The sperm issue came up and I thought, "Oh God, it was me." Then I would go back to, "I'm a fucking healthy individual, how does this happen?" Everything I read up about sperm is about your health and the choices you make.

("Remember, last summer, there was a time where our doctor brought up my egg quality, that there may be an issue with them and that could play a role…? So it wasn't just you…")

Do you feel different this time around? How?

I guess the first pregnancy you don't know what to expect, but this time we know. Now, Tyler is at an age where we can leave him in a different room to play, but it's the "on all the time" aspect that worries me. I like my time and to do my things, so we will have to make sacrifices.

I think, also, this pregnancy went fast because the world was falling apart and our minds were going 1,000 mph. And I think we are personally busier — me with administration and you with your teaching and side business. Plus, we have Tyler so there's less down time. Thinking back to ham, egg, and cheese sandwiches and watching Nurse Jackie when Tyler was a newborn, I know it won't be anything like that with two kids running around.

Do you feel that the pandemic took away from our pregnancy joy? Even in the slightest?

I feel it did more for you because you weren't able to see your family as much. I'm a guy so it's not a thing, but for you, going to Connecticut and seeing your family like we usually do wasn't possible.

"I think the *biggest thing* is just
how proud of you I am. I'm so
happy it was successful for you.
This is such a terribly *gruelling*
process, not just in the physical
toll it takes on your body, but
the *emotional toll* of managing
this while all of your other *life*
stressors continue on around
you (a stressful job, raising
a *3-4 year old* who was nearly
the size of you already, Dad

getting sick). It takes *incredible* fortitude to go through this, especially when most of your *social support* system lived in another state. You, and all the women going through this, are *amazingly strong* and I hope that in you telling *your story* it will help other women and families feel supported and *understood.*"

—Sonia

Afterword

I wasn't sure how to wrap up this book, but I felt like I needed some sort of closure. I know it may have been uncomfortable to read about my pregnancy when you might be going through treatments still. I didn't want to write too much about the birth of my daughter either, but I felt that it was the natural ending to this book.

Our daughter, Isabella Laurel, is one step forward in our healing process. Thankfully, we had a smooth, scheduled C-section and she was born on September 2, 2020. I remember every single second of anxiously waiting for her to come out, and when we finally heard her cry, we squeezed each other's hands and just sobbed; cried tears of joy, tears of thankfulness, tears of relief. Even though my husband was the only one allowed to be with me at the hospital, it was so peaceful just soaking in this incredibly special moment.

I want you to know, though, that I'm still you. I still carry the pain because I went through it.

Three months after having my daughter, my medications that needed refrigerating were still sitting on the shelf — ironically next to my pumped breast milk. Talk about a picture being worth a thousand words.

That's something right there. I don't know why I hadn't gotten rid of them yet. Maybe it reminded me of my strength. Maybe it reminded me of my journey. Maybe it also reminded me that I'm still afraid. I'm still afraid that this is a dream. I don't think those visions and memories of taking those shots will ever go away. I'd be willing to bet that it's a form of PTSD. We've gone through a lot and it's going to take a lot to wrap up those memories with a nice little bow and move on.

After my daughter was about three months old, I got a bill in the mail from RMA for my embryo storage fee. I totally forgot about it; I forgot that I still had to pay to store it. Of course, I know I signed the endless documents for IVF before it all began and I remembered this would happen, but it was still like a little pinch. It took me all the way back to that retrieval and everything we had gone through to get where we are now. My point is, I will always remember my struggles because they have made me who I am today.

Your journey may or may not end with getting pregnant and having a baby. I came to terms with that before I started the procedures for IVF, but I took those chances anyway. If I hadn't tried, I would have wondered, "What if?" However, I had to do a lot of digging and soul searching — and therapy — to get to that point and be "okay" with it. Would I have been okay with having just one child? I don't truly know that answer because my life has turned out otherwise, but I can tell you I was preparing myself for it.

The thing is, I thought about that every single day.

Every. Single. Day.

Infertility takes over everything when you are in the thick of it. I thought that maybe this was the way it was meant to be. Maybe this was God's plan for me, even though I wasn't happy about it. I really did let go and leave it up to Him. Let me tell ya, it made the weight on my shoulders a little lighter. This doesn't mean that I wasn't still stressed out about it or that I stopped thinking about it. Anyone who knows me personally knows that I like to have things in control, I like order, and I put a lot of pressure on myself to do my best. With that said, infertility doesn't really fall into those categories.

Something I wish I had done differently was to celebrate. You might be thinking, "What the hell are you talking about?" Well, I've found a whole community of women on Instagram who openly share every aspect of their infertility journey, and it's not all negative. There is support, there are celebrations, there are people to talk to. I didn't realize all of this until I finally let go of the embarrassment and shame of it all. When I told myself I was done living in secrecy and wanted to bring awareness to this, that's when I really found that I was not the only one.

I wish I had explored all of it sooner. I wish I hadn't been afraid to talk about it and show people how common this actually was. Women were posting about their shots at night, their transfer days, their IUI days, pictures of them at their doctor's office with the ultrasound screen behind them — *smiling*. I guess I just saw the whole experience as one great big negative. I wish I had seen it differently. I should have been proud of myself for injecting three needles into my stomach each night. I should have celebrated the fact that I made the decision to get help and go to therapy. I should have commended myself for picking up the pieces month after month and trying again, and again, and again.

I can tell you now, though, that I'm damn proud of myself for going through it all. I know how hard it is to hear and see another pregnancy when that's all you want but can't have. All I can say is that I wish you the absolute best. I wish you courage and strength to get you through and to keep you moving forward, no matter what it may look like.

Each of us has a different life plan. We may have the same goal, but I'm sure we have had a variety of experiences on this infertility journey. My heart goes out to you. I hope your path leads you to peace, whatever that may be.

Remember, *it takes a village* — or plenty of tools in the toolbox — to get you through. Here are some things that *comforted* me, gave me strength, motivated me, or just helped me have a *good cry.* I hope these *help you,* too.

Resources for You

Music

"Girl," Maren Morris
"Anything Could Happen," Ellie Goulding
"Work Bitch," Britney Spears
"Work It" and "Lose Control," Missy Elliott
"R-E-S-P-E-C-T," Aretha Franklin
"If It's Meant to Be," Florida Georgia Line and Bebe Rexa

Books

Dear Girls, Ali Wong
This is Me, Chrissy Metz
Infreakinfertility, Melanie Dale

Podcasts

WHOA, That's Good, Sadie Robinson

Notes

Introduction
1. Charles Coddington, M.D., "Secondary Infertility: Why Does it Happen?" (Mayo Clinic, 2021), accessed March 29, 2021, https://www.mayoclinic.org/diseases-conditions/infertility/expert-answers/secondary-infertility/faq-20058272.

The Journey's Over
1. Catherine Donaldson-Evans, "Subchorionic Bleeding During Pregnancy," What to Expect, December 9, 2020, https://www.whattoexpect.com/pregnancy/pregnancy-health/complications/subchorionic-bleeding.aspx.

The Two-Week Wait
1. Rachel Gurevich. "Surviving the Two Week Wait When You're Trying to Conceive." Very Well Family. April 26, 2020. Web. March 29, 2021. https://www.verywellfamily.com/two-week-wait-survival-tips-1959987.

Moving Forward
1. Brené Brown, "Brené Brown delivers a message of hope to 2020 graduates," The Today Show, May 28, 2020, https://www.today.com/video/brene-brown-delivers-a-message-of-hope-to-2020-graduates-84026437796.

Insurance
1. World Health Organization, "Infertility," who.int, 2021, September 14, 2020, https://www.who.int/news-room/fact-sheets/detail/infertility.

2. "Infertility Stats You Should Know," Fertility Answers, 2021, accessed April 10, 2021, https://www.fertilityanswers.com/13-stats-know-infertility/.

Coronavirus and Pregnancy
1. World Health Organization, "WHO-convened Global Study of Origins of SARS-CoV-2: China Part," who.int, 14 January–10 February 2021, pp. 6-11, https://www.who.int/publications/i/item/who-convened-global-study-of-origins-of-sars-cov-2-china-part

Bibliography

Brown, Brené. "Brené Brown delivers a message of hope to 2020 graduates." *The Today Show,* May 28, 2020. https://www.today.com/video/brene-brown-delivers-a-message-of-hope-to-2020-graduates-84026437796.

Coddington, Charles M.D. "Secondary Infertility: Why Does it Happen?" Mayo Clinic, 2021. Web. March 29, 2021. https://www.mayoclinic.org/diseases-conditions/infertility/expert-answers/secondary-infertility/faq-20058272.

Donaldson-Evans, Catherine. "Subchorionic Bleeding During Pregnancy," *What to Expect.* Last modified December 9, 2020. https://www.whattoexpect.com/pregnancy/pregnancy-health/complications/subchorionic-bleeding.aspx.

Gurevich, Rachel. "Surviving the Two Week Wait When You're Trying to Conceive." *Very Well Family.* Last modified April 26, 2020. https://www.verywellfamily.com/two-week-wait-survival-tips-1959987.

"Infertility Stats You Should Know." *Fertility Answers,* 2021. Accessed April 10, 2021. https://www.fertilityanswers.com/13-stats-know-infertility/.

World Health Organization. "Infertility." *World Health Organization*, 2021. Last modified September 14, 2020. https://www.who.int/news-room/fact-sheets/detail/infertility.

World Health Organization. "WHO-convened Global Study of Origins of SARS-CoV-2: China Part." *World Health Organization*, 2021. 14 January–10 February 2021. https://www.who.int/publications/i/item/who-convened-global-study-of-origins-of-sars-cov-2-china-part

Acknowledgments

There are so many people that have supported me throughout this process. I want to thank my family and friends for being there when I need you most. To the infertility community on Instagram, you helped me at my lowest without even knowing it — thank you. I want to send some big shoutouts, though, to a few particular people that helped make this dream of mine possible.

First, thank you to my publishing team, The Self Publishing Agency. Thank you to Megan, Ira, Stephanie and Elise. You all have helped me to be more confident in sharing my story and helped to make it what it's meant to be, for all to read.

Second, I want to thank my friends, Vicki Nungesser, Katie Benedict, and Kelly Niland, for their contributions. Each one of these incredible women shared pieces of their own journeys with infertility and it truly helped transform this book. I thought it was equally important to share others' perspectives, as no path is the same. I also wanted to show readers that within your own circle of family and friends, there is sure to be someone going through this.

Third, I want to thank my sister, Sonia Altavilla. She helped me during some very difficult times while going through treatments, whether it was pumping the jams or dancing alongside me, every moment was important.

Lastly, thank you to my husband, Jonathan. Thank you for supporting me with, not only this publishing process, but, more importantly, being strong for both of us as we struggled for years. Thanks for overcoming your fear of needles and getting those shots done every morning. Thanks for taking care of whatever it was when I was too tired or too emotional. And thanks for loving me, even when I wasn't the easiest to love.

Forever and Always.

About the Author

Simona Altavilla Moss lives with her husband and two children in Central New Jersey. She is an elementary teacher by day and an entrepreneur by night. She has a passion for teaching children, while also running her small business of art and handmade goods. She is on a mission now, to help bring infertility into normal conversation. This is her first book, and she hopes that her story sheds some light on this difficult road to motherhood.

You can find out more about her and her work at
www.simonajaltavilla.com or on Instagram @simply_simona

Made in the USA
Monee, IL
01 August 2021